Ya Big Black Purse

Drama of a Greek Mama

by Tassie Kalas

Edits & Layout & Publishing via Van Velzer Press
Cover digitized by miblart
Chapter Illustrations by Joni Zavitsanos

ISBN: 978-1-954253-09-4
Printed in the United States of America

Van Velzer Press
Americana with a Twist

VanVelzerPress.com

Dedication

To my three beautiful children, who give my life meaning and purpose.

To my mom and dad, who made sure I felt safe and loved.

To my family and friends, who make life worth writing about.

May we always laugh without fear of the future and have happy stories to share.

And to Yaya. May her memory be eternal.

This book is for you.

Directory of Funny Stories

Enjoy yourself. It's later than you think.
                                      -Socrates

Home is where the heart is, whether it's bursting with life and chaos, or turned into a peaceful retreat. And home is where this story begins.

Growing up isn't easy, but growing older takes courage, a sense of humor, and lots of margaritas ... Here's how I survived...

Sometimes you have to grow up to appreciate how you grew up.

Growing Up Greek

Everyone knew the Hokey-Pokey led to hanky-panky. That's why my father forbade me to go to our 7th grade end-of-year roller skating party. Boys, the kind with long hair and bell-bottom jeans, would be there. Although he trusted me (because I didn't wear hippie clothes or green eye shadow like my friends from school) he didn't trust other people, meaning anyone not from Nafpaktos, his village in Greece.

Of course, I asked my mother first, after practicing in front of the mirror for twenty minutes to master a believable look of indifference. She was having her third cup of Maxwell House, leafing through the latest issue of Prevention Magazine. Her lips were carefully stained with Orange Crush lipstick. That meant my dad would be home soon. I had to work fast. I could hear the coffee pot percolating in the background. *No. No. No. No.* It sputtered as if taunting me with the certain answer to come.

"Mom, the school is having an end of the year celebration at the skating rink Friday." I prided myself for not calling it a party. "It's kind of required. So, I can go, right?" I shrugged as if my life didn't depend on it.

The cup of coffee shook in her hand. Born in Houston, she was second generation Greek-American, and although she was terrified of a confrontation with my dad, I could usually count on her to be sympathetic. Her nose crinkled as if she smelled something unpleasant. "You'll have to ask your father."

Her doubtful tone caused my false bravado to crash in a heap at her feet. It was my very last chance to see

Donny Donaldson, a cute blonde boy in my class. "I want to go. I *have* to go!" But I knew I'd already lost the battle.

The scenario never changed for any of these events. This special night my heart pounded in anticipation as I waited for my father to come home. I tried to judge his mood while his thick, strong arms reached for my mother and he kissed her on the lips. I observed his body language, waited until he seemed relaxed, then ran up to him and kissed him on the cheek, lingering until he took a sip of coffee and bit off the tip of a sesame covered kouloudakia. I took a deep breath and began buttering him up as if he were a Greek pastry. My stomach was as knotted as the twisted cookie he held in his hand.

"Dad, look!" I waved an essay I'd written called *My Hero, My Dad* under his nose. "I got an A on my paper!"

"That's great *agape mou!*" He glanced at the report as if it were written in a foreign language, which to him it was, and took another sip of coffee while my mother looked on, a worried expression on her face.

I took a deep breath, inhaling the smell of his Old Spice and my fear. My younger sister and brother, sensing drama, dove under the kitchen table. Yaya and Poppy, my grandparents who lived with us, disappeared into the other room. It was now or never.

"ThewholesixthgradeisgoingskatingandcanIpleaseha vethreedollars?" I spit the words out before I lost my nerve.

His eyes widened. His mouth gaped open. It was as if I'd just announced to him the Greeks had not invented democracy. He shook his head as if he hadn't heard correctly. "There will be boys there?"

I nodded my head in resignation.

"Greek boys?" He looked at me expectantly.

I examined my Earth Shoes.

"No!" He cocked his left eyebrow and threw up his right hand for emphasis, karate chopping the air in front of my nose, his signal that no conversation would follow.

My essay fluttered to the floor. I ran into my room, slammed the door, and threw myself onto my bed. Sobs wracked my body. Everyone assumed their roles. My mother avoided me. Yaya tried to cheer me up by sneaking make-up samples to me from Joske's where she worked at the Revlon counter. Poppy sat quietly eating canned peaches at the kitchen table, wondering what all the drama was about.

Later that night, my dad slipped a twenty-dollar bill under my door before he went to bed, a peace offering that said he loved me, but all it would take was one boy in roller skates from the wrong family circling around his precious, pure daughter to ruin me forever. He believed I'd thank him one day when the perfect Greek boy came along, preferably one whose roots could be traced all the way back to my father's hometown.

So I prayed for a Greek boy, a handsome figure who would ride up in a golden chariot, possessing a magical key to release me from this gilded cage I was locked inside. I wanted to go steady so badly I could feel the weight of his gold-plated ID bracelet on my delicate wrist, could taste the saltiness of his kiss. I asked God to send me a soul mate, a confidante; someone tall so I could wear platform shoes and still place my head on his shoulder when we slow danced.

Instead, four months later he sent Celeste...

I was sitting in Mrs. Papacantpronounce's 7th grade Sunday school class after church that fall, daydreaming about Donny Donaldson and fantasizing that he was

Greek. She was just getting fired up about the evils of Ouija boards when a short girl with curly red hair entered the room in a cloud of Love's Baby Soft and sat in the empty seat beside me. I tried not to stare. She looked so different from all the rest of us with our predictable dark Greek hair.

The other kids eyed her openly. It was rare anyone new braved our cliquish class, and if they did, they seldom stayed long. It wasn't that we were unfriendly, but our church families went back generations. We knew where we stood with each other like our parents and grandparents did.

After class, Mrs. Papa pulled Celeste aside. I tried to squeeze by them, eager to escape into the hall for a stale sugar cookie and a Dixie cup full of lemonade, but she placed a firm hand on my shoulder.

"Celeste moved here from Pittsburgh with her family." Mrs. Papa's eyes bore into mine. "Show her around. Introduce her to the other girls." She ignored my discomfort. "I told her about the GOYA dance this weekend. Can you see if your family can give her a ride?"

I avoided her piercing stare. She was also the youth group director of the Greek Orthodox Youth of America and no one ever dared to say no to her. I wasn't about to be the first. "I guess."

"Good!" She clapped her hands together. "You girls make plans. I'll see you both Friday night." She turned abruptly and marched out of the room.

Celeste's shoulders slumped. "Sorry about that." She brushed imaginary lint off her plaid skirt. "Don't worry. We don't have to go to the dance together. I'm sure you already have plans to go with your friends."

I hadn't planned on going to the boring GOYA dance. Being the tallest wallflower at the church wasn't my idea of weekend fun. Besides, all the Greek boys were short. And none of them were anywhere as cute as Donny Donaldson.

Asking my mom (aka her asking my dad) if I could go would be a nightmare. Worse yet, he would probably say yes since it was at the church and he could stand in a corner and talk business with the other fathers, give all the boys the evil eye, and keep a close watch on his oldest daughter at the same time.

"I don't think my dad will let me go."

"You're lucky! My mom will probably *make* me go. She's worried about me making friends."

"Where's your dad?" I was fascinated that her mother would actually encourage her to interact with boys. I figured Pittsburgh must be a lot more exciting than Houston.

She looked down at her feet. "He's not here."

I fantasized what I could get away with if my dad were out of town. "When's he coming back?"

Her face reddened. "He's not. My parents got a divorce."

"Oh." I'd never met anyone before whose parents were divorced. As difficult as my father could be, it was hard to imagine my family without him. I reconsidered the new girl and had a sudden urge to protect her. She could use a friend and I had more than enough dad to go around. "You know what? Let's go to the dance." My new friend and I walked to the hall for punch and cookies, the top of her curly auburn head barely reaching my shoulder. "Who knows? It might be fun."

I devoted the rest of the week to getting ready for the dance. My mother took me shopping at Palais Royal and we agreed on a floor length pink dress with spaghetti straps. Bonne Bell bubblegum flavored lip-gloss, pink blush and gold strappy heels I found in her closet completed the ensemble. Friday night I wobbled into the living room to show my family.

My mother made me twirl in a circle, tilted her head and wrapped one of her shimmery shawls over my shoulders and across my chest.

Dad whistled in approval. "You look beautiful." He nodded at my outfit. "That's how you should dress. Not in those hippie clothes you wear to school."

My brother and sister peeked shyly at me from the sofa. Poppy looked up from the newspaper he was reading and Yaya ran up and spritzed Jontue perfume on my neck. Wobbling in my borrowed heels, I towered over my entire family.

I was still flustered from the attention when the doorbell rang. I teetered as fast as my shoes would allow and opened it in time to see a woman in a white Oldsmobile speed off, leaving her daughter on my doorstep.

"I like your dress," Celeste said looking up at me and smiling.

"I like yours."

She wore a long blue and white gingham dress and matching blue sandals with cork platforms. A silver mood ring with an aqua stone sparkled on her finger. While any other girl in the same outfit might have looked like she'd just stepped off the set of *The Wizard of Oz,* Celeste managed to look hip and cool.

She glanced over my shoulder and waved. "Hi, everyone."

The entire family had followed me to the door, eager to meet this new friend.

"Come in!" my dad bellowed at Celeste who cowered by a potted plant. He gestured at my mother. "Get the girls something to eat before we go. They look hungry."

"*Uhm.*" Celeste hesitated and looked over at me. "I ate at home."

I shrugged and shook my head at her innocence. It was futile to argue. As if by magic, the kitchen table was filled with platters of beef and ribs and potato salad from Dad's restaurant. Mom sliced a chocolate cake into hearty wedges.

"Sit down." Dad waved a barbequed rib in front of Celeste's nose, sauce dripping dangerously close to her dress. He speared a chunk of beef with the tip of a carving knife and offered it to her. "Best barbeque in town! Not like that shoe leather everyone else is serving." He waited until Celeste took a polite bite then sprung his first question at her, "So, what part of Greece are your parents from?"

Celeste swallowed and accepted a plate of cake from my mother. "Ikaria."

"Island people." My dad grunted. "That's ok."

"We really need to go now." I wrung my hands, anxious to leave the house, but Celeste was humoring my mother now, and working on her second slice of cake. Force feeding my new friend and grilling her about her family— I thought the night couldn't get any worse.

Then we arrived at the dance.

Dad dropped us off and promised not to return for at least two hours. I didn't exhale until I saw his black

Cadillac go down the street and turn the corner. Though I had spent the last week planning for this night, I didn't want to go inside.

Celeste reached for the door and cracked it open a few inches. *Staying Alive* blasted from within. We slipped inside and paused in the darkened hall. I inhaled the familiar smell of Sunday coffee blended with the musk of teenage hormones.

"I feel sick." Celeste's skin took on a greenish tone under the party lights and she clutched her stomach.

"It'll be alright," I said without conviction. We crept closer to the dance floor.

A disco ball spun slowly overhead casting prisms of sparkly light over the shadowy forms swaying to the beat. They were all clustered underneath the basketball net. Mrs. Papa handed out root beer floats from behind the refreshment table. She spotted us, nodded and waved. A few boys looked over, then leaned their heads in together and laughed.

"I have to pee." My heels clicked over the slick tile towards the restroom, Celeste was trailing close behind, groaning as I raced into a stall.

"We can't stay in here all night." She checked her reflection in the mirror from every angle. "I mean, what's the worst that can happen?"

I joined her at the mirror, fluffed my feathered bangs with my fingers, and reapplied my lip gloss. I'd grown up with this crowd and was afraid to admit what could happen. We could be laughed at, ignored all night, or worse yet, asked to dance. "We need a game plan. If it gets rough out there, we meet back here, ok?"

Celeste nodded grimly.

I briefed her before we headed out. "Just stay away from the older boys. We call them the pack. They've gotten in trouble for drinking before."

Celeste's eyes widened.

"You probably won't have anything to worry about." I examined both our reflections in the mirror and shook my head. "We're not their type. You'll see what I mean."

The minute we poked our heads out the door, Mrs. Papa waved us over. She handed us both a frosty mug and admired our dresses. "Don't you girls look nice." She gestured towards the dance floor. "Now have fun."

We carried our dripping mugs across the floor and stood awkwardly, watching the dancers. The first notes of *Brick House* blasted through the speakers and the boys gave each other knowing looks. An older one made a beeline towards a curvy girl named Kiki and asked her to dance. The pair gyrated to the beat, doing a version of the bump, their hips bouncing off each other seductively. A crowd formed around them. In our world, Kiki *was* a brick house, and the GOYANs were fixated on her spacious second story.

"*She's* their type." I pointed to Kiki, dressed in formfitting black jersey, the only one of the girls who had graduated from a training bra to an underwire, seemingly overnight.

Celeste slurped nervously on her float.

A hyper boy with a manic smile approached and grabbed her hand. She looked at me with alarm, chugged the rest of her drink and thrust the empty mug at me. Before she could protest, he pulled her out onto the dance floor and circled her, dancing a caffeinated jig around her stiff body. Then he seized both her hands and whirled her around and around getting dangerously close to Kiki's burlesque show.

"Hey, watch where you're going!" Kiki shouted at the new couple on the floor and bumped them brazenly with her womanly hips.

I watched helplessly, embarrassed for my new friend. If Kiki was a brick house with an impressive upper balcony, I was a towering high rise with sticks for arms and legs. Twirling out of control on the dance floor in her gingham checkered frock, Celeste resembled a tiny Kansas farmhouse sucked up by a tornado.

Slumping into a chair at one of the round tables, I kicked off my mother's heels and looked down at the flat front of my dress. It seemed I would never stack up.

As the Commodores worked themselves into a frenzy, shouting at us to shake it, I searched the dance floor for Celeste. This would be a good time for another bathroom run. Unfortunately, a boy from Sunday school caught my eye. Brown cords and a wide collared white shirt was his version of dressing up. He was the one who drilled Mrs. Papa weekly, wondering if *thinking* about sinning was just as bad as *actually* sinning. If it was, no doubt he'd already broken seven of the Ten Commandments watching Kiki's kinky moves.

When the first faint notes of a new song started, he whispered something to his buddy and began walking my way with a gleam in his eye.

Panic seized me when I recognized the ballad. *Stairway to Heaven!* Topping eight minutes, it was probably the longest song ever recorded. Girls across America feared being asked to slow dance to the sultry tune. If Donny Donaldson himself materialized in front of me in a leisure suit and asked me to dance to it, pure anxiety would force me to turn him down.

The stress was just too great. *Hurry up, Celeste!* I rose from my chair, fight or flight taking over my body, and prepared to run for it. If she didn't know enough to make a dash for the bathroom, God help her.

In my haste to get away, I ran right into the boy in the cords.

"Wanna dance?" He leered up at me eagerly, his gold cross glittering under the disco lights.

Even without my heels his head barely reached my shoulder. I was shaking my head no when I spied Celeste on the dance floor, Manic Boy holding her close. I could see her hand resting on his shoulder, the aqua stone in her mood ring turning a murky shade of black. Loyalty trumped my better judgment. "I guess..." Celeste might need me and I'd be of no help to her hiding in the ladies room.

Cord wrapped his arms around me.

I caught Celeste's eye over his head and tried to send her a telepathic message. *There's a feeling I get when I look at Celeste and my spirit is crying for leaving.* I improvised the words to the song rocking over the speakers.

Cord pulled me closer to him. Unable to stand face to face with me, he awkwardly settled his cheek on my collarbone and closed his eyes. I breathed in the musky scent of Brut with a splash of testosterone and started to sweat.

As the beat picked up, Manic Boy grew even more animated, spinning Celeste like a top on the dance floor. I strained to read her expression as she twirled uncontrollably. What was she trying to tell me? *Ooh, it makes me wonder...*

Her mouth was moving as if she wanted to say something, her head lurching in time to the music. Manic Boy spun her furiously one last time, and dizzy from the movement, her body weaved back and forth in slow motion. Time seemed to stand still.

Then barbeque, cake and root beer float mixed with teenage terror spewed out of her mouth like hot lava erupting from Mount Santorini! The gross mix was splattering all over her dress and her partner's shoes.

I pushed Cord away and hurried to help my friend, but before I could reach her a familiar form bulldozed his way onto the dance floor.

"Dad? What are you doing here?" Embarrassment burned my cheeks.

"You didn't really think I'd leave you at your first dance all alone, did you?" He put one protective arm around Celeste and another around me, and escorted us across the dance floor. "Boys will be boys, even if they are Greek."

As he guided us through the crowd, he caught a glance of Kiki struggling with her dance partner in the shadows, and his body tensed. He stormed up to the pair, removed her dance partner's wandering hand from her backside and growled at the older boy. "Keep your paws to yourself!"

Kiki blushed and threw him a thankful look, held her head up high and hurried off the dance floor. All the GOYANs chattered at once but he silenced the entire mob with a single raised eyebrow.

Mrs. Papa abandoned her station at the refreshment table and rushed towards us. She thrust a wad of napkins at Celeste, then made her way to the light switch and with two sharp movements, flicked the disco ball off and the fluorescent overhead lights on. Under the harsh light of reality, the dance floor that had been bathed in prisms of colored lights moments before transformed back into a scuffed gym floor. Half-filled, discarded mugs stuck to the tables in puddles of melted ice cream, ties and jackets hung over the backs of folding chairs, limp and forgotten.

On the way out we passed by Kiki who was sobbing softly outside the ladies' room. "They only want me for one thing!" she cried aloud to no one in particular, her cleavage heaving with emotion.

"Well maybe two things," I whispered to Celeste. But we air hugged the girl goodbye and promised to sit with her in Sunday school later that week.

My dad settled us into the Caddy and drove us straight to Walmart. He handed Celeste a twenty-dollar bill and told us to go in and buy her a change of clothes. Her gingham dress reeked with the pungent reminder of her first dance and he was probably afraid it would ruin our appetites.

"Buy her something nice." He turned up his eight track tape and shooed us from the car.

Back at the house he told us the best thing for an upset stomach was more food, so Celeste and I ate another helping of barbeque and the rest of the chocolate cake. She called her mother and asked permission to spend the night.

"Your dad's scary," Celeste said when we were alone. "But in a good way."

I had to agree. The night may have been filled with more drama than dance, but having my first sleepover and laughing with my new friend about it was worth the humiliation we'd suffered. We giggled long into the night like old friends, about boys and parents and church and school, and made plans for the next weekend. *Who needed an old skating party, anyway? I don't even know how to skate!*

That night, not sure whether it was because of our similarities or because of our differences, with every story we shared and every laugh we smothered behind our hands so we wouldn't wake up my parents, we began to form a friendship as faithful and forgiving as family— one that would fortify us forever.

When my head finally hit the pillow that night, I closed my eyes, took a deep breath and smiled. For the first time in my life, I felt like a normal teenager.

Taking the Lead

Looking for some "hot stuff" baby, this evening or any evening, in the foreseeable future, was now officially banned. According to our Sunday school teacher, the dancing inspired by that popular song was inappropriate—at least on church property. After all, if Donna Summer danced off a cliff, would our youth group follow her, gyrating all the way down?

In addition, after witnessing our moves on the dance floor, the next week at Sunday school, Mrs. Papa set out a formal decree that members of the Greek Orthodox Youth of America were required to take dance lessons. We should be dancing *with* each other, she said, not *at* each other.

"There will be no more bumping bottoms on the dance floor." She stood before us with her hands on her ample hips and waited for our tittering to subside.

"I'd pay to see *her* do the bump," a boy from the back of the room mumbled under his breath. Laughter erupted causing Mrs. Papa to scowl.

"There will be absolutely no groping each other during slow songs." She seemed confident that if we took proper lessons, we would be so busy dazzling each other with our new moves the next dance wouldn't be a disaster like the last one.

"And finally, some items were found left behind at the dance Friday night." She held up my mother's shimmering shawl, which had lost its luster in the light of day. "This was forgotten under a table by the dance floor."

Celeste looked at me and smiled. Mrs. Papa placed the wrap on my desk.

She pulled an assortment of smaller items from a cardboard box on her desk. Loose keys, a lone sock, a collection of combs went unclaimed.

"I know something Celeste left behind!" A boy retched and the class snickered. "Bet she doesn't want *that* back."

I glared at them in defense of my friend.

"And these were found in the ladies room by the sink." Mrs. Papa waved a pair of falsies in the air, the mounds of breast-shaped padding larger than her head. The entire class gasped in unison and hooted with laughter, except Kiki, who spent several long seconds examining her nails.

Mrs. Papa informed us that every Saturday for the next six weeks we were to meet at the Westbury Square Dance Studio at seven o'clock for dance lessons. One of the GOYAN moms was a close personal friend of the owner and had graciously arranged the classes for us. The first one was even free. The girls seemed more excited than the boys at this opportunity.

"Saturday night fever!" Kiki hollered with approval. "John Travolta, look out!"

"I don't need dance lessons." Cord scowled from his desk. "I already have all the right moves."

"And after each lesson we'll meet at Rumpleheimer's for ice cream." Mrs. Papa's eyes settled on Celeste. "I encourage all of you not to eat before class."

I snuck a peek at Celeste and rolled my eyes. The thought of lessons didn't thrill me, but the chance to hang out with my friend for six weekends straight did.

The following Saturday, six girls and four boys who were forced by their mothers to attend lined up in front of a mirrored wall at the dance studio. To Kiki's delight, our instructor, a John Travolta look alike, strutted out in tight white pants and jazz shoes. His gold chains glimmered in the fluorescent light.

He snapped his fingers and directed us to follow him in a simple step. "And forward, two, three, kick! Back, two, three, kick!" We moved like a herd of cattle, stumbling and running into each other. He took one look at our motley crew and sighed.

"I can see we're going to have to start with the basics." He tossed his dark curls and sashayed to a record player in the corner of the room. "But first I want to show you how it's done." He placed an album on the turntable. The Bee Gees blasted from the speaker. He held out his hand with a flourish and a woman dressed in a flowing skirt pirouetted up to him and batted her eyes. The two had clearly tangoed before. "My assistant and I will demonstrate what you should be able to do at the end of six weeks."

The woman looked strangely familiar. Celeste squirmed beside me.

The pair did the hustle and grapevine across the room. Then Mr. John took the woman by the hand and spun her towards him, her skirt billowing out with the movement exposing her thighs and leaving nothing to our thirteen-year-old imaginations.

Mrs. Papa gasped.

My hand flew to my mouth. "Oh my gosh," I whispered to Celeste, "is she wearing underwear?"

"Yes!" Celeste hissed with surprising force. "It's a flesh-colored body suit."

Mr. John instructed us to pair up with partners next. Kiki shimmied up to the one boy over 5'4" and claimed him for herself. Two other boys made a dive for Mrs.

Papa's daughter Evy, a petite girl, and the only blonde at our church.

I shifted uncomfortably. Cord wandered up to me holding a folding chair under one arm. He placed it at my feet and climbed up on it. Now magically a foot taller than me, he smiled triumphantly, proud of his cleverness. I glared up at him. One well-timed bump of my hip would send him flying off that chair. Mr. John read the expression on my face and hurried over to intervene. He scowled at my cocky partner and tapped his foot until Cord slithered down. Then he posed the boy's arms, tilted his chin and nudged him towards me. I reluctantly positioned myself in his arms.

"Fever night, fever night, fever..." Cord looked up at me as he sang the next phrase, nodding his head for emphasis. "We know how to do it." Then he hustled me forward when he should have hustled me back and I tried to correct him. "Hey, I'm the man!" He tightened his grip on my hand. "You're supposed to follow me!"

"Then *be* a man." I stiffened my body and struggled to get us on the right count. I'd rather be a wallflower for the rest of my life than follow someone who couldn't pick up the beat.

Mr. John swooped in. "I'm splitting you two up for irreconcilable differences." He sent Cord across the room to dance with a timid girl in the corner and with no other available options, placing Celeste with me. He studied our height difference, clucked his tongue, looked at me and stated the obvious, "You'll have to be the boy."

While Mr. John instructed the other girls to relax and let the males take charge, he taught the boys and me to lead with our torsos and form strong frames with our arms uplifted, all the while keeping an eight-count beat in our heads.

He instructed the ladies lucky enough to be dancing with us to close their eyes and surrender completely to their leading men. "Don't think!" he reminded the females, but only Kiki seemed to enjoy this part of the exercise.

"Ouch!" Celeste cried out and opened her eyes. "You stepped on my toes again."

Mr. John ran up. "May I cut in?" He reached for Celeste's hand and performed a perfect partner hustle, spinning her under his arm and twirling her back out. "You dance just like your mother."

My eyes widened and my head spun towards his assistant in the flowing skirt. Her curly hair and olive skin, the same deep-set eyes, the resemblance had been there all along. Celeste's mother! I mentally compared her to my own, trying to imagine my mom wearing something other than her elastic-waisted jeans with a man other than my dad and the difference was jarring.

Mr. John gave Celeste a final twirl and admired her technique. "You just need the right partner."

Don't we all? My eyes wandered over the GOYANs who by now had given up on their partners and were line dancing, hustling towards their reflections in the mirror, pausing to shake their hips from side to side, pointing their index fingers at the ceiling. *I Will Survive* boomed through the room. *But I'm sure not going to find him here.*

The song ended and I headed for the door. The pressure to find a perfect partner was over, at least for now. We were done spinning and twirling and Celeste could safely enjoy a root beer float without fear of vomiting. I started for the ice cream shop, the others hustling to keep up with me. I might not be a good follower but that would be to my advantage anywhere but the dance floor.

"Hey," Cord shouted. "I know a shortcut!" He pointed a disco finger in the opposite direction.

Ignoring him, I kept walking. The others were happy to let me lead.

Yaya's Big Black Purse

It was comforting growing up to know my heroes were only a hallway and a holler away. My grandparents lived with us. They were my strongest allies, always available to applaud my achievements, fight my fears, and wipe my tears. While my protective Greek parents kept me safe, Yaya and Poppy bent every rule to make me happy.

As a result, I grew up feeling secure and loved.

Poppy, an intellect who spent his spare time with his regal nose buried in *World Book Encyclopedia*, attended all of my school programs, proudly wearing his favorite gray suit, a feathered fedora topping his head.

While he was fair-skinned and refined, Yaya was solid and robust, with jet-black hair and an olive complexion. Although my mother only ventured down the familiar road to school and back, Yaya chauffeured me through town, navigating the Houston freeways in her cinnamon Oldsmobile. No friend, no mall, no adventure was too far away for my grandmother.

She was the strongest woman I'd ever met. I was convinced she had superpowers, but instead of a cape, she wore a magical black power purse strapped on her shoulder and filled to the zipper with things we never thought we'd need, but somehow, always did. Bad day, bad breath, bad smell? Yaya waved her hand over the bag, reached inside and pulled out a tissue, a peppermint, perfume. **Power Purse and Yaya to the rescue!**

Every Sunday she put on her best dress—navy, because it was slimming—and took me to church.

"Light a candle." She tossed coins into the collection basket and handed me a white taper. "Kiss the icon."

I knew from Sunday school we didn't worship icons. They were, after all, paintings on wood. We kissed them to show respect for what they represented, Christ, the Virgin Mary, angels and saints. Yaya had a wall full of them in her bedroom, some passed down for generations. I would often sneak into her room to stare up at those soulful images.

I watched her praying beside me at our usual pew and wished I had her blind faith. While Poppy was born in Kefalonia, Yaya's family was from Patmos, that sacred Greek island where St. John wrote the book of Revelation. Because of the religious slant of her family tree, and the fact that all her prayers seemed to be answered, we suspected God blessed Yaya with a stronger than average dose of grace. Here is an example of that grace:

I was in my twenties and living on my own when my mother called with bad news.

"Poppy's had a stroke."

I raced to the hospital. Poppy lay on the bed, a tangle of tubes hooked up to his frail, blue veined arms. He gestured for me to draw near. I leaned forward, my ear hovering over his lips.

He moaned then shook his head in frustration.

My eyes welled with tears. "It's ok. We'll talk later."

"Mwa-waa-waa!" His face grew red.

I shook my head in despair.

He grabbed my arm and pulled me closer, his nails digging into my skin. "Money. Hidden in closet. Coat pocket." His eyes darted around the hospital room. "For Yaya..."

Not wanting to think about money at a time like this, I patted his hand, noticing the familiar gold cameo ring he wore. As he drifted off to sleep, I remembered being a little girl, feeling the weight of that ring when he took my small hand in his, the zing it would send up my arm when he'd tap my knuckles with back of it.

He called me his Agape to Poppy. Repeating the words out loud, the rhyme rolling off my tongue, I recalled setting up the checker board for our nightly game at the kitchen table, watching the glint of gold on his wrinkled hand glide and jump across the red and black squares. *Poppy's love.*

His eyes fluttered open for a moment and he spoke again, this time more clearly. "I had the most beautiful..." he drew a deep breath as I leaned in closer, anxious to catch his next word, "...dream."

Though I left the hospital knowing where to find the family treasure, for the first time since I was a little girl, I felt lost. When Yaya called the next day to ask me if I wanted to go to church, I figured she must have been feeling the same way.

"There's an icon at the little Orthodox church in Bellaire," Yaya lowered her voice to a whisper, the family signal to pay close attention, "it's *crying.*"

"Crying?" I worried weeping icons were taking her grief and her faith to another level. "That's crazy, Yaya." I looked up at the ceiling and sighed. "I'll be right there."

Mom and Yaya were waiting when I pulled up at the house. They piled in and we drove to the church in silence, Yaya was fiddling with the strap of her purse, deep in thought. None of us had uttered a word of our plan to anyone else. Our unspoken pact was that if we were all crazy, it was best kept secret within the family.

I lit a candle for Poppy, whispering a prayer for him. In a hushed corner of the church, a group of people stared up at an icon of Jesus.

I stood back and watched as my mom approached, squinted at the icon, then covered her mouth with her hand. Yaya marched up to it, nodded her head, and made the sign of the cross. I stepped one tentative foot closer and peered at the picture of Jesus. His eyes glistened with tears that dripped like diamonds slowly down his face to the bottom edge of the frame where cotton balls had been placed to catch the sacred liquid.

Yaya plucked up a damp cotton ball and stuffed it in her purse. "My icons would never cry." She looked down at the gold cross around her neck and shook her head. "I don't have enough faith."

We drove back to the house in stunned silence, the miracle fading as we returned to our daily lives. Mom made a pot of coffee. Yaya dabbed her icons with the cotton ball from her purse. I returned to my little one-bedroom apartment to process the unbelievable events of the day in private, hoping the tears were a heavenly sign Poppy would be healed.

The next morning my phone rang at 6am. I lunged for it in alarm.

"You're not going to believe this," my mom's voice was shrill.

I held my breath. "Is it Poppy?"

"Yaya's icon." My mom took a deep breath. "It's crying!"

I sped to their house in the early morning light and ran straight into Yaya's tiny bedroom. I found Mom and Yaya standing in front of the wall of icons pointing to one and murmuring. The glittering drops were unmistakable.

Jesus wept!

"We have to tell someone. A priest?" I looked at Yaya.

She folded her arms across her chest and shook her head.

I lightly touched the stream of tears. "But it's a miracle." This time there was no doubt in my mind. "We can't keep it to ourselves."

Yet in the end, we did. It was Yaya's miracle and she didn't want the attention, good or bad, that it could bring our family. The tears continued for three days, then disappeared as mysteriously as they had arrived.

Poppy died shortly after. He was the first person I'd ever lost and my heart ached each time I walked by his favorite chair. He never got to spend the money he'd hidden, but it helped my grandmother long after he was gone. The icon made me see his real treasure wasn't stashed in an old coat pocket, any more than Yaya's real strength was tucked in the depths of her shiny black purse. **Their real power was love, and it worked miracles when it was shared.**

I may never see another icon cry but I'm thankful for this faithful reassurance. I know I'm never alone. To this day that memory is a tiny shred of proof I carry around in my heart, my invisible superpower I can pull out to make me feel safe and secure.

I realize now the icon was never meant to save Poppy.

The icon was meant to save me.

Sticks and Stones

As a young girl, I longed for Leigh, ached for Ann and was desperate for Deborah. For a short time in junior high I was mad about Marie. I had a yen for Lynn as a teen, but in college I developed more sophisticated taste and hungered for Hope. *Oh, to grow old as Olivia,* I wrote in my diary.

I knew I was different from all the other girls the first day of Kindergarten. My teacher, Mrs. Frizzell, plump and middle-aged with a frizzy halo of faded red hair curled about her face, growled out roll call. I studied the other girls in my class. Blonde, bobby socked and blue-eyed, they raised their hands one-by-one as she crooned their names, pretty as flowers, insisting we use our full names that first day to get to know each other better.

"Cheryl Ann," she called. "Mary Elizabeth, Laura Lynn." She looked down at her clipboard and paused. Her eyes scanned the room with suspicion. "T-assie?" She spit out my name like it left a bitter taste in her mouth. "Am I saying it right?"

My face grew hot as I nodded.

The class tittered and turned to me in unison. "Tassie, Lassie." A boy guffawed at his cleverness. "Beware of the dog!"

"Tassie, what?" Mrs. Frizzell tapped her yardstick on the floor. "What's your middle name?"

Humiliated, I hung my head, stared at the graffiti on my desk and wished I could crawl under it. I whispered a response, "Just Tassie."

She clucked her tongue, muttered something under her breath about some parents and returned to roll call. "John Michael? Matthew Mark?"

That night at dinner I blamed my parents for cursing me at birth.

"What's wrong with your name?" My father speared a slab of feta with his fork. "You're named after my mother. May her memory be eternal." He swiped at his eyes. "She was a saint. A real saint."

I pictured a short, squat woman dressed all in black trudging up a mountain path in Greece, waving her cane at a herd of goats blocking her way, a golden halo floating over her head.

"Everyone has a middle name!" I looked at my mother for support. "Everyone! What am I supposed to fill out on the forms at school?"

She looked at my dad across the table, shook her head and studied her fingernails.

"Tell the school your middle name is the initial A." My dad wiped his mouth and got up from the table, signaling the end of the conversation. I was just Tassie A, and that was that.

Dinner was over. So was my life.

"But what does the A stand for?" my best friend wanted to know the next day at school. "Ann? Angela? Amy?"

"It doesn't STAND for anything."

"Alice? Audrey?" She made a face. "What if it's Agatha?"

The shame of my name followed me all through high school and college. Although I didn't accept my middle name initially, in time it became part of me. It even came to define me. I made straight As in school. My blood type was A positive. I had a Type-A personality. Like my longer second toe and my near-sighted eyes, I didn't like my name, but short of risking the wrath of my deceased grandmother, or breaking my parents' hearts, there was nothing I could do to change it.

Even getting married wasn't the answer. My *last* name was the last thing I wanted to change. I liked the Greekness of it, the link to my family heritage. But my Scotch-Irish American fiancé had tradition on his side. Most women in the 80s still left their identities and their family name at the altar.

I tested out what my new name would sound like, letting the vowels and consonants roll off my tongue like candy. Mr. and Mrs. Happily Married. Mrs. Happily Married. Mrs. Married. As a Mrs., maybe I wouldn't miss not having a middle name.

Finally, after months of planning and monogramming, the day came for us to go to the courthouse to get our marriage license. I was floating on a cloud of premarital bliss when my fiancé came to pick me up from my parents' house.

"You'll need your birth certificate," my mom said slipping a yellowed envelope into my hand. She glanced nervously at my dad who was sitting at the kitchen table scowling at the newspaper and lowered her voice. "You might want to open it now."

My fiancé peered over my shoulder as I pulled out the twenty-five-year-old document and carefully unfolded it. My heart warmed when I saw my parents' shaky signatures, the date and time of my birth. Then I froze when my eyes settled on the name. Tasia Albert Kalas.

"Who's Tasia?" my future husband whispered.

"My grandmother," I hissed. "In Greece."

"What are we doing with your grandmother's birth certificate?"

"It's *my* birth certificate."

"Then what's with the Albert?" He looked at me accusingly. "You told me you didn't have a middle name."

"I told you it's the letter A."

He snorted. "I mean, it's not even Alberta or Albertine."

I let that sink in. What were my parents thinking? Didn't they understand the importance of a name? That it holds the power to shape and define a person, to influence how others look at them for the rest of their life? I vowed I would never do this to my child.

"Maybe you could change it," he suggested, as if it was a shirt that didn't fit right.

"I'm not changing my name." I glared at the man I was about to marry. "And I might not change my LAST one, either."

My mother hung her head. "I should have told you sooner. But you wanted a pretty middle name so badly. You wanted to be like all the other little girls." She sighed. "I thought you'd be mad at us."

"I just can't believe you never told me." I walked over to a mirror on the wall and stared at my reflection as if seeing myself for the very first time. "Hello Albert," I said to the glass. "It's nice to meet you."

I blinked and a chubby cheeked man laughed back at me, his ample belly bouncing. *Hey, hey, hey. It's Fat Albert.* I rubbed at my eyes and did a double take. Superimposed over my face a mad scientist with a shock of unruly gray hair, nodded wisely. *Albert Einstein.* **Albert.** A fat name. A nerdy name. I shook my head and glowered into the glass. A short, muscular man appeared in the reflection beside me, one eyebrow cocked. Then he winked. *My dad.*

"It's Greek tradition." My dad pounded his thigh for punctuation. "All the babies get the father's first name as their middle name. Girls, boys, it doesn't matter."

I shook my head.

My dad looked at me and smiled, his eyes growing misty. "Besides, when I saw you for the first time you were so beautiful, I wanted the whole world to know you were mine."

I considered his words. There was meaning behind this name. He wore it proudly, like a crown, and I wanted to wear mine that way, too. It stood for family, tradition, heritage. I smiled at my dad and nodded my head. He had made a name for himself, and so would I.

He got up from the table and waved his hand in the air. "You can call yourself anything you want. You can change your name, you can change your mind, but you can never change who you are or where you came from."

Dad was right. We had a beautiful, big, fat Greek wedding, one Albert walking the other Albert down the aisle, and for the time being, my middle name was forgotten.

But history has a way of repeating itself. Three years later I found myself staring at another birth certificate, this time from my hospital bed in the maternity ward. Exhausted, I shrugged my shoulders and shoved the paper at my husband. "You decide."

The nurse walked in with my newborn son and smiled at us. "Have you decided what you're going to name him, yet?" She placed the tiny bundle in my arms.

I looked down at my new baby and stroked his shock of black hair. Uncurling one of his fists, I placed my finger in his hand and he gripped it with surprising strength. Then he opened his eyes, stared up at me and let out a mighty roar.

At that moment, Michael and Patrick, Nicholas, Ray, and all the other boy names we'd so carefully considered from the *Popular Baby Names* book flew out the window of Methodist Hospital on stork's wings, never to be seen again.

"Albert," I said.

My husband shook his head and filled out the form for the nurse.

Moments later, the door burst open and my dad strode into the room, grinning from ear to ear, carrying a to-go bag from Pappasitos and smelling like chicken fajitas.

"This is for you." He placed the Tex-Mex in lieu of flowers on my bedside table and nodded at the nurse. "I left a bag at the nurse's station, too." He cocked one eyebrow at the nurse. "You take good care of my daughter, now." His eyes filled with tears as he beamed at his new grandson.

The nurse hurried off, her rubber soles squeaking on the tile floor. My heart welled as I watched my dad making ridiculous faces, bonding with his first-born grandchild.

"Look at that face. Those eyebrows! You can tell he takes after our side of the family." He shrugged an apology at my husband, then turned his attention back to his heir. He stroked the newborn's tiny fist, and winced in surprise when his grandson grabbed his meaty finger and squeezed until it turned blue. "Strong, too!"

My dad smiled broadly and burst out with the only children's song he knew, singing loudly and off key. "*How much is that* skilo *in the window? The one with the curly tail? How much is that* skilo *in the window? I do hope that doggie* skilo's *for sale.*" Then he sang the entire song again, this time in Greek. Bob Merrill would have been proud. The newest member of the family looked up at him, scrunched his face and howled.

"He's loud! We don't have to worry about this one not speaking his mind." He settled on a cracked vinyl chair and turned to me. "So, what did you name him?"

Bubbling over with happiness and hormones, I couldn't wait to tell him. Finally, for once in my life, I felt sure I was going to gain his approval and secure his everlasting love.

My husband was eager to please him, too. "You're going to love this!" he paused to look in my dad's eyes, then announced, "Albert."

"Great! So what's his name?" My dad leaned forward in anticipation.

"Albert," my husband said slowly.

My dad drew out his answer. "What?"

"His name."

"What's his name?"

"Oh for Pete's sake!" I cried. "Albert! We named him Albert! After you." I studied my dad's face, sure he would melt with emotion.

Instead he had an emotional meltdown.

He looked at me, horrified. "You named him Albert? Why'd you do that?"

My mouth hung open. "We named him after you." I looked down at my sleeping baby and tears welled in my eyes. My voice caught in my throat then squeaked out, "We thought you'd be happy."

"I hate that name! I can't even pronounce it." My dad waved his hands in the air, his face growing red. "It's not even my real name, just something they gave me at Ellis Island when I came over. I was only thirteen!"

"What do you mean?" My adrenaline rush from giving birth evaporated in an instant, and my shoulders slumped under my new floral nightgown. "I thought Albert was your name. I thought you named *me* Albert after you."

My husband patted my arm. "I'm just going to slip out for some coffee." He grabbed his Game Boy from my overnight bag and scurried out of the room.

"My name's Angelos. They thought that was too Greek and changed it to Albert." He gestured to his grandson. "Give the boy an easy name. Joe or Tom or Bob."

I was crying now, a heap of hormones. "Those names don't mean anything." Sensing my discomfort and his grandfather's disapproval, baby Albert began to wail.

"That baby's starving," my dad said. "Somebody call the nurse."

"He's not hungry." I cradled my baby to my chest. "He's having an identity crisis!"

The nurse rushed in to find three generations of Alberts huddled together on the hospital bed, taking turns crying and comforting each other. She waved a piece of paper in the air. "You didn't finish filling out the birth certificate," she shouted over the ruckus. "You left the middle name blank."

The room grew quiet and I looked at my dad, deep in thought. He winked at me.

"No middle name," I said.

"Are you sure?" The nurse persisted. "He won't be like the other kids in school. He may feel left out."

I looked down at baby Albert and rocked him in my arms. He stared back at me, his eyes dark pools of indigo, waved his fists in the air, and cocked one well-defined eyebrow just like his grandfather.

I kissed the top of his head and inhaled his sweet scent. This was no average Joe I held in my arms. He would have no problem carrying on the family name.

"I'm sure." I nodded my head at the nurse. I knew the importance of a name. Growing up with an unusual one built my character and gave me strength. Nicole or Marie, Ann or Leigh, may have taken me down an easier, prettier road I wasn't meant to travel. My son would never question who he was or where he came from.

My husband might propose something different—maybe we'd add a name from his side of the family, too. But for now, in this moment, there was no question. I looked down into my baby's eyes and his sweet face tugged at my heart.

"Just Albert."

Mother's Day Out

Like many stay-at-home moms in the 90s, with three children under the age of four, I was desperate for contact with the outside world. While I longed for adult conversation— and a round or two of adult beverages— my daily routine consisted of babbling babies and Barney reruns. As much as I loved my new life as a mother, I would have gladly traded in my collection of stretch pants for a hot shower, an afternoon nap and a meal that didn't consist of frozen nuggets shaped like dinosaurs.

I was a shell of the woman I used to be. I once shopped at the Galleria for the latest fashions, now I appreciated midnight jaunts alone to Walmart for a pack of Luvs. Lunches once enjoyed with girlfriends at El Patio were replaced with tearful telephone conversations between feedings. *Is green snot normal? How about green poop?* Highly anticipated date nights with my husband were cancelled after exhausting play dates with neighborhood mamas with dramas of their own.

For fun, and if I'd gotten more than three hours of sleep the night before, I'd unfold our gargantuan Graaco double stroller, rub us all down with Coppertone and settle my two oldest into the vinyl seats. They would clutch handfuls of Cheerios in their tiny fists while I'd pack the diaper bag with enough Wet Ones to wipe the bottoms of the entire neighborhood, strap my youngest to my chest, and treat us all to a walk in the park. But with rabid dogs lurking behind every bush and infectious mosquitoes the size of pterodactyls swarming around our faces, we may as well have been on a treacherous trek through *Jurassic Park*, instead.

So we spent most days in our pajamas with me in a 90's version of a muumuu and smearing on lipstick seconds before my husband walked in from work. I had everyone fooled that I was Supermom. No one had to know my cape was a milk-stained terry-cloth robe with emergency pacifiers stuffed in the pockets, except my three children and me, and they weren't talking enough to be incriminating. Yet.

When my mother called and offered to come over to help me with the children one fine day, I leapt at the opportunity. I looked forward to her visits. I knew she didn't go anywhere without reinforcement and would arrive with my grandmother and Aunt Dorothy in tow. Finally, adults would outnumber children. Finally, I'd get a much-needed break.

I fantasized about what I could do with a free afternoon. I envisioned myself wrapped in a fluffy white towel enjoying a Serenity Spa Package at an upscale salon. "You can't be a mother of three!" the sexy masseur would exclaim as he took too long kneading my childbearing hips. "You have the body of a supermodel. Must be from all those walks to the park." I'd have a mani-pedi and meet three of my girlfriends for martinis at the chicest happy hour in Katy, where we'd ignore the jealous looks from other woman as we fended off male attention. I might not be able to duplicate *Sex and the City*, but *Sex and the Suburbs* was a possibility.

The thought of free babysitting catapulted me into action. Frantic, I looked around the house. It looked like a daycare had exploded leaving behind a collection of sippy cups, abandoned toys and a school of Goldfish smashed into the carpet. Like a madwoman I dashed around the room scooping up puzzle pieces, baby bottles with fuzz covered nipples, discarded bits of clothing of various sizes and caffeine-coated coffee mugs.

"Mommy?" My son was peering up at me from behind a colorful Playmobil fort with a worried look on his face. He placed a protective arm around his younger sister. "You're scaring us."

My daughter put her hands on her hips. "I'm hungwy!"

"There's no time for this!" I raced to the refrigerator, grabbed three Yoplait Twix yogurts and tossed them to the toddlers. "Yayi will cook you a nice meal when she gets here."

I flew into the children's rooms and threw open dresser drawers in a panic. Surely there was one clean outfit. *Dear God, do we own one pair of matching socks?* Somehow, I managed to get each child dressed. I suspected my son was wearing his sister's jeans, but selfishly decided it would be worth sending him to therapy sessions in the future if it guaranteed my sanity today.

As I sped by the hall mirror, I caught a glimpse of myself and froze. My hair was frizzed around my face. Not only that, it was flecked with particles, like I'd been a referee at a toddler food fight. I fought to comb my fingers through the nest with no success. An entire zoo of animal crackers could be trapped in my hair and I wouldn't discover it until my youngest graduated from high school.

Staring at my reflection, I used a chipped fingernail to scrape a squished green pea off the front of my faded t-shirt. This was not the face of a woman from a sexy TV series. This was the disturbing image of a woman who'd been *Home Alone* for far too long.

A hot shower and I'll be good as new. I planted the two oldest in front of the TV turned to their favorite purple dinosaur. I settled the baby into her playpen with her favorite toys and a sippy cup of juice. She stared up at me all eyebrows and lips and smiled. I held my breath. *Maybe I'll have time to use conditioner.* But when she noticed me tiptoeing out of the room, she threw her cup at my back and let out a bloodcurdling scream. *Super-De-Duper!*

I scooped her up, carried her into the bathroom and plopped her on a towel on the floor outside the shower. She watched fascinated as I did a G rated strip tease with Barney's booming bass in the background. She squealed as my food-splotched t-shirt flew through the air, then giggled as I fought to free myself from black leggings.

"Peek-a-boo!" I covered my eyes with my hands and she mimicked my move. I wiggled out of my granny panties and dove into the shower, howling from the shock of the icy water on my naked body. *One day I'll have the luxury to wait for the water to heat up!* Racing to finish before she crawled out of the room, I worked up a sweat while I worked up a lather.

I vowed that as soon as my mother set one white Reebok through my door, I was out of there. I would speed off into the sunset in my soccer mom Suburban, Journey blasting on the radio, the wind whipping through my freshly washed hair.

Somehow, in supermom mode, I managed to get the children, the house, and myself presentable enough for company. When the doorbell rang less than an hour later, the two oldest, wearing color coordinated outfits from Baby Gap, raced to the door. I followed behind them, all smiles, the baby slung stylishly on my hip. My silver bangles clinked softly as I opened the door.

"Hi Mom. Hi Aunt Dor...."

Before I could say another word, my mother thrust a platter of sugar cookies in my hands and kneeled to embrace her grandchildren, fighting the others for the first hug. "My babies!" She body blocked Yaya and grabbed a child in each hand, leading them to the sofa. "Yayi missed you!" She pulled out a new board book from her purse and began reading aloud.

"You can't have two!" my aunt called out then scuttled after them and squeezed onto the couch by my mother. "I get one!"

Yaya, not to be outdone by my mother and aunt, struggled to pry the baby's arms from around my neck. "This one's mine!" She made kissing noises and lunged at my youngest, who burrowed her face into my chest and screamed.

I took my grandmother by the elbow and led her to the other sofa, propping her two stocking feet on the coffee table. We sat side by side, the baby still ignoring her, until she saw the strand of pearls that glowed around Yaya's neck and reached out to grab them. The older woman held out her tan weathered arms, and her great-granddaughter went to her, stuffing a fistful of pearls into a tiny mouth.

When I saw the look of pure bliss on Yaya's face, I forgot about happy hour with my friends and focused on this quiet, happy minute instead. Fighting the urge to race out the door so I wouldn't be late for my nail appointment, I allowed myself the luxury of being still.

For one perfect moment, four generations sat content in the almost tidy living room. In that precious instant, no one was hungry or thirsty, or wanted anything but to enjoy the peaceful company that was family. I studied the three calm women before me, took a deep breath, and sighed with satisfaction. They'd all survived motherhood, and so would I.

"I don't know how you do it." My aunt surveyed the living room. "The house is so clean."

My mother looked up from the book she was reading. "And look how cute the children are dressed!" she patted my son on the knee and lowered her voice, "but is that a pink butterfly on Albert Alston's jeans?"

I shook my head and leaned back on the couch, my eyes too heavy to hold open.

"I wuv you. You wuv me. We're a happy famiwy..."

The last thing I remembered before shutting my eyes was my daughter singing along with Barney while the credits rolled on the TV.

All You Can Eat

Yaya understood me like my overprotective Greek parents never could. Despite her age, she remembered what it felt like to be young. I could count on my grandmother to become my partner in crime when I had to hide things from my mother and to rescue me later if I was caught. She was always there in a faded apron to soothe my growing pains, usually with homemade food she served up with a side of love.

While my mother worried about me growing up too fast, Yaya seemed to enjoy growing up along with me. She and my Poppy moved in with us when I was thirteen, and while I should have been wary of an extra two sets of adult eyes watching over me, my grandparents became my instant allies instead. Perhaps co-conspirators is a better description.

Yaya smuggled cosmetics to me from her job at the Revlon counter at Joske's, showing me how to use them. She supplied my friends and me with bottomless snack bags of Goldfish and Teddy Grahams, and chauffeured us all over town in her big Oldsmobile. We drove to skating rinks and parties, listening to KC and the Sunshine Band. She chimed in like one of the girls when we talked about cute boys.

"I'll tell you who's good looking." Yaya would smile, toss a few chocolate Teddy Grahams in her mouth, and nod her head over the steering wheel. "Magnum P.I., that's who."

She let me practice driving in that same car, never complaining, even when I locked the keys in it with the motor running...and didn't notice until I'd shopped for several hours at Meyerland Mall.

Although she'd only gone to school through the 6th grade, Yaya knew the importance of an education. She backed me up when I wanted to go away to college. Despite my dad's demands that I stay home and go to the U of H, Yaya drove me to Ft. Worth for a TCU campus visit. She cried the loudest and longest when I was accepted and wrote me weekly letters in her shaky handwriting, filled with news from home.

When I returned for holidays and summer breaks, exhausted from the grueling demands of school and tired of a semester of bland college food, her home-cooked meals comforted me almost as much as her warm hugs did. A firm believer that food was love, Yaya cooked all my favorite dishes in the short amount of time I'd be home.

In the mornings the tantalizing smell of smoked bacon sizzling on the stove awakened me. I'd drift by the kitchen and snatch up paper-thin slices of salted potatoes fried in olive oil straight from the pan, and swipe buttery brown biscuits from the counter before they cooled. Later in the day she might entice me with steaming pot pie, bubbling with bits of chicken and tender vegetables seeping out from the flaky crust, or heaping slabs of pastitsio bursting with buttered noodles and meat sauce and drenched with cream.

She loved every boyfriend I ever had...all two of them...and approved of my husband even though he wasn't Greek.

"I like him," she whispered loudly as she sized him up. "He looks like Rocky." She squinted up at him and squeezed his bicep. "Before he was beat up."

When I was pregnant with my first baby, Yaya showed up on my doorstep on my due date, unannounced, clutching her huge black patent leather purse and a family-sized bucket of Kentucky Fried Chicken, extra crispy. She didn't want me to be alone, or hungry, just in case I went into labor. She'd heard a young woman from church gave birth in the Junior League bathroom the week before, so wasn't taking any chances with her first great-grandchild.

After my babies were born, she lived for Tuesdays, when I would pack all three kids up for my mom and Yaya to babysit. She'd wait for our visits, sitting on the front porch for hours, oblivious to the weather, through wind and rain and 100% Houston humidity, until my white Suburban pulled up in the driveway. Then she would race to the car, entice her great-grandchildren with warm sugar cookies, and whisk them away before my mother even knew we'd arrived.

I loved her with all my heart, and I returned the favor when, years later, *she* needed to do things behind my mother's back. She'd given me starter wings decades ago, so I could fly (at least a few feet away from my parents' watchful eyes) knowing I had a safe place to land. The least I could do was empower her in small ways as her own wings grew weak and her independence began to slip. I snuck her frozen margaritas, even though she wasn't allowed to have salt, much less alcohol. I took her for mani/pedis and spicy Mexican food, and pretended I wasn't mortified when she picked up one of my Cosmopolitan magazines to read and started discussing it.

"No, Yaya, I haven't read *21 Mind-Blowing Sex Moves You've Never Tried Before.*" I could feel my face flush from embarrassment. "And I haven't *tried* any of them, either." I ignored her disappointed look, snatched the publication from her hands and hid it under a pile of Better Homes and Gardens. "I only subscribe to that magazine for the fashion photos, anyway."

As the years went by, I pretended not to notice the toll aging played on her. She was shrinking, her bangle bracelets hanging loosely from bony wrists, and no amount of food seemed to help. She couldn't hear my mother anymore yet somehow, could still hear me. I also pretended not to notice she was slowing down. She hated using her new walker, but it had become a necessary accessory. I held her elbow and her signature large handbag as she navigated the wheeled device, still eager to leave the house on our weekly outings.

One thing that hadn't changed was her appetite. She still hungered for food as well as adventure. One of her favorite places to go was the neighborhood Cicis for the all-you-can-eat pizza buffet. Her eyes would grow big as she took in the feast before her. Salad and soup, miles of pizza with various toppings and breadsticks drenched with butter and cinnamon for dessert. All you could eat for only $4.99—a dollar taken off for senior citizens! Yaya loved a bargain and you can't beat a buffet for quantity value.

Once a week my mother and Aunt Dorothy (identical twins) packed up Yaya and drove all the way to Katy to see the kids and me. Because my mother wouldn't drive on the freeway, this epic journey across town that might have been a thirty-minute drive for Yaya in her glory days, took them about three hours with Mom dodging potholes on Houston's feeder roads in her antique car.

I'd make them hot apple crumble and serve it to them with ice cream the moment they walked through the door, exhausted and travel weary, and they'd inhale the dessert like they'd been lost in a desert, or worse yet, Houston, on a hot, humid day. We'd spend the rest of the afternoon shopping then redecorating my house and admiring the kids...but we all knew the grand finale, the sole reason for the visit...was a trip to Cicis.

Somehow, everyone in my party agreed that after a grueling day of shopping with three young children and a walker in tow, nothing satisfied more than a greasy wedge of pizza and an ice-cold Coke. This one particular day was no different as we pulled up to the restaurant and piled out of the car.

Yaya shuffled to the door in anticipation, pushing her walker, my mother and aunt flanking each side, bodyguards wearing matching elastic waist jeans. The pair had the double duty of making sure she didn't slip on the walk down the buffet line and policing the pizza she placed on her plate. Whispering like little wrens about the fat content in cheese, they watched their cholesterol, sugar and salt intake, feeling their mother should, too.

"Hello ladies." The friendly young manager smiled a bright welcome and swiped the Formica counter with a bleach-soaked dishrag. "Welcome to Cicis." His hazel eyes glazed over as my mother and aunt quizzed him on the fat and calorie content of each pie.

Yaya blushed (her cheeks turning pink) plopped an orange tray on the line, and inched her way to the salad, sneaking peeks at him over the sneeze guard as she designed a perfect leafy arrangement on her plate. She pushed her tray forward, paused over a pile of pasta and peered back at the manager, admiring his strong build from behind.

I made a mental note to hide all the Cosmo magazines before her next visit.

A few feet later, she stopped to ladle a cup of soup into a bowl and observed him greeting more new customers. Suddenly, she threw up one hand and slapped her forehead. "Bonanza!" she announced to no one in particular.

I looked at her in alarm. "Yaya, you'll spill your soup!"

She leaned closer to me and lowered her voice saying, "Little Joe."

Still confused, I turned to my mother and aunt for translation.

Aunt Dorothy sighed and whispered in my ear, "Michael Landon. She thinks he looks like that actor from the old TV western." She stole a glance at the young man who was trying his best to pretend he couldn't hear us. "The cute one."

Little Joe cleared his throat behind the counter. Customers were piling up behind us so I hurried my group down the line. Ironically, all my kids *would* eat at a place like this was Alfredo pizza. All I *should* have here was salad. But under Little Joe's watchful eye, Mom, Aunt Dorothy and Yaya painstakingly loaded their trays with as much as they thought they *could* eat, even planning to go back for more.

We settled down at a long table and the feeding frenzy began. The twins ate an entire ham and pineapple pizza with no cheese, then returned for second helpings of chocolate brownies and cinnamon rolls. The kids ate just the pizza part of three Alfredo pies, leaving crust mountains on their plates, then begged us for quarters to use in the mini arcade room.

Yaya rummaged around in her magic purse, pulled out a handful of coins, and distributed them to her great-grandchildren. She watched them race off to spend her money on Pac Man and super balls, then looked down at her untouched plate and shook her head. "I'm just not hungry, after all." She frowned. "It's a shame to let all this good food go to waste. I'll ask that nice man for a to-go box."

The twins looked up from their plates, horrified. "Mama, no!" they cried in unison, pointing to a sign on the wall. "There's no plate sharing and NO taking food home."

Yaya rolled her eyes. "I'm sure he'd understand--just this once." She struggled to stand.

"Mama, don't you dare!" My aunt grabbed her arm. "You'll embarrass us. Just leave it."

I glanced around to see if anyone was paying attention to our unruly table. Only Little Joe seemed to be looking at us with concern, wearing a sour look on his face like someone who'd eaten too many anchovies.

Yaya's shoulders slumped in defeat.

My heart sank as I saw the expression on her face. There was no wasting of food in her house. The freezer was bursting with leftovers frozen beyond recognition, half-eaten servings of something or other too good to throw out. After all, there were starving children in Greece! My own husband was probably starving at home. But I knew she wouldn't argue. My mother and aunt were a formidable force when they teamed up, and Yaya, in her weakened state, had to share a freezer and a home with them.

The kids ran back to the table, bouncing their new super balls. Mom and Dorothy herded them together and started for the door, holding their stomachs and moaning about eating too much. They waited by the exit as I helped an unusually quiet Yaya to her feet. I placed her oversized black purse on the crook of her arm, positioned her walker in front of her and took her elbow as we made our way to the exit.

"Goodbye, ladies." Little Joe strolled towards us and opened the door with a flourish. Nodding at Yaya, he curled his lips into an automatic smile. "Come again."

Yaya beamed up at him and batted her eyes. If her knees would have allowed it, she might have curtseyed. She leaned towards him, placed a hand on his arm, and confessed in her most flirtatious voice, "I have pizza in my purse."

Little Joe's eyes widened and his mouth dropped open. A flicker of disgust flashed across his face as he glanced at my grandmother's purse. I groaned when I noticed a wad of greasy napkins peeking out of the corner of her bag.

He hooked his thumbs into his belt and glowered down at us.

Mom and Dorothy, who had never broken a rule in their lives, covered their mouths in a synchronized move and burst out in unison. "Mama!" The pair grabbed the kids and bolted out the door.

I knew this visit to Cicis would be our last. They would be too humiliated to ever return, no matter how many buy-one-get-one-free coupons they got in the mail.

"Yaya, quick! Let's make a run for it." I caught the manager's eye above her head, expecting him to laugh at my joke. "Before he calls the police."

But Little Joe didn't crack a smile. He shook his head and gestured to the sign on the wall.

I shot him my scariest death glare, reserved for whiney children and disagreeable spouses, reached into my pocket, and drew out my secret weapon, a pointer finger honed from years of motherhood. I raised my eyebrows. *Careful, dough boy.* He might be cute Little Joe now, but working this job, he was only a few pepperonis away from turning into his portly brother, Hoss. *You mess with Yaya, you mess with me!* I puffed out my chest, which wasn't all that hard to do after an all-you-can-eat meal of pure carbs. *You want a pizza me?*

He stepped back and raised his hands in the air. "I don't make the rules, ladies."

Yaya patted a gray curl over her ear, straightened her back and tilted her chin. Years seemed to melt away from her body as she deserted her walker and sashayed out of the door, leaving a trail of garlic butter perfume behind.

I hid a smile as I folded her walker, tucking it under my arm as I followed her to the car.

The ride home was tense. Mom and Dorothy sat in the backseat with pursed lips, arms folded, refusing to look at us when we got into the car. The kids were sniffling in the third seat, still convinced their mother and great-grandmother were going to be hauled off to jail. I glanced over at Yaya seated beside me. She was grinning like a schoolgirl and rummaging around in her purse.

"I don't know about you, but I'm starving." She pulled out two garlic cheese sticks, dripping with butter, and handed one to me.

I looked at my lifelong partner in crime, and smiled. "Thelma and Louise, that's who we are!" I revved up our get-away car.

Then we tapped our breadsticks together across the front seat arm rests, toasting our teamwork, and drove off into the sunset.

Fowl Play

The Thanksgiving after my grandmother passed away, my family was too chicken to tackle a turkey

Yaya barely weighed more than a Butterball herself, yet she spent days preparing feasts for us, which we would gobble up before she even had time to sit down. In our Greek family, food was love, and Yaya loved us with all her heart.

We considered going cold turkey that first Thanksgiving without her.

"I'll bring home some barbecue," my dad offered.

My mother hadn't inherited the cooking gene. All she could offer was, "I could make no-boil lasagna."

I stared at my parents, horrified. My happiest childhood memories were waking up Thanksgiving morning smelling Yaya's turkey roasting and admiring the lavish spread on the table. Turkey cost 35¢ a pound in November, for Tom's sake! I vowed to give my family a Norman Rockwell dinner if it killed me.

Going grocery shopping was a workout. Dozens of women wearing yoga pants leaned into the frozen cooler, digging through mountains of smaller turkeys, struggling to reach the heavier ones at the bottom. I elbowed my way through, zeroed in on a plump bird and wrestled the woman beside me for it. Breaking a sweat, I hoisted two-ton Tom into my cart and sprinted to the checkout counter. Seven dollars and seven minutes later, I was cramming frozen fowl into the fridge to thaw.

Days later, my daughter caught me at the kitchen sink staring in horror at the naked bird. Mounds of pale goosebump-covered flesh quivered under the harsh kitchen lights. It reminded me of myself in the Macy's dressing room trying on the first bikini of the season.

"This won't hurt a bit." I plunged my hand in, searching for the neck. Grasping it in my fist, I pulled and twisted, but the bird wouldn't budge. Bracing my feet on the cabinet, I strained with all my might until the neck broke free with a gruesome sound, sending me sprawling onto the tile floor in a puddle of turkey juice and tears. This never would have happened to my grandmother. I pictured Yaya wearing her floral housedress, shaking her head at me.

"Mom, are you crying?" All three children surrounded me now. "What's that gross thing in your hand?"

Somehow, I rose to the occasion, summoned Yaya, and lovingly spread olive oil over our main course. I sprinkled it with oregano and paprika and stuffed it full of onions, celery and carrots. Hours later, my house smelled like Yaya's kitchen.

My family tore into the juicy meat and pronounced me chief turkey maker. For life. They loved it so much they requested one for Christmas and Easter, too. While other family members offered up store-bought rolls and canned sweet potatoes mashed into a Pyrex dish, every holiday from then on, I woke at dawn to battle the beast into a feast.

Fifteen years later, I'm still thankful for the role. Yaya would be proud.

Still, I'm dying to give someone else a chance.

Women of Walmart

In the beginning, life was roses and chocolates and sunset walks on the beach accented with handwritten love notes. Then it was smiling babies, one after the other, a home filled with happy laughter, honey-do lists.

"How'd I get so lucky?" my handsome husband asked me every night before we fell asleep, one arm draped over my shoulder.

I was the happiest woman in the whole world.

Until I wasn't.

He still kissed me goodbye every morning on his way to work. We shared phone calls at lunch, talking about the kids' schedules and what we would eat that night. He was there, but not *there*, like a switch had been shut off, dimming the twinkle in his eye. He walked around like a man who didn't particularly care for the shirt he was wearing and couldn't wait to take it off.

I broke down one day against my better judgment, certain I had the solution for a man flirting with forty. "How about we buy that motorcycle you've been wanting?" When that suggestion didn't get his juices revving, I suggested counseling, a new hobby, a romantic getaway for two.

"You don't get it." He shook his head, a miserable look on his face. "I don't want a getaway for two. I need a getaway for one."

He packed a small suitcase and promised he only needed a few days to get his head straight. I pretended nothing was wrong for the sake of the children, certain he would change his mind and be home soon. If they thought it was unusual Daddy had been gone for days, they said nothing, absorbed in their elementary school world.

"If you don't come home, we can't work on this. I can't save us by myself," I screamed at him on the phone, begging him to come to his senses. "You're not just leaving me. You're leaving three children under the age of ten." I paused as a fresh wave of hot tears flooded down my face. "How can you look at yourself in the mirror?"

"They're fine," he said. "I told them all about it over pizza the other night." He waited for me to stop shrieking in his ear. "I'll be coming home tonight to pick up some things for my new apartment."

I slammed the phone down. Anger consumed me as I took a mental inventory of the house. I considered changing the locks so he couldn't get in, holing up in my bedroom indefinitely with the children. I imagined meeting him at the door with a baseball bat and a rabid pit bull. *Not my Lenox Autumn china, Buddy. Not my twelve-piece set of Oneida Michelangelo flatware. Not on your life!*

Then suddenly, the solution became Waterford crystal clear.

"Kids!" I called up to them wiping my face with the back of my sleeve as the evil plan played out in my head. "We're going to Walmart."

"Can I buy a toy?" my youngest daughter asked as we piled in the car.

"Today we're buying things for Daddy," I said. "I know he told you he has a new apartment." *How dare he make that announcement without me there!* "We both want you to feel at home when you visit." *Every other weekend when my heart will be ripped from my body.*

"We're going to buy some stuff to help him decorate." *So he'll leave my things alone!*

We parked and strode into the megastore. An elderly greeter smiled brightly, then frowned when he saw my grim expression. Everywhere giant smiley faces, a sharp contrast to mine, grinned, inviting us to enjoy everyday low prices. I grabbed a shopping cart and wheeled down the aisle, road rage pulsing through my veins as an elevator version of *I Will Survive* blared from the speakers.

"Daddy needs a lot of things." I slowed down in the bath section and fingered a selection of rough, thin towels. I looked at my youngest daughter. "Baby, which ones do you like?"

"Ooh, these!" She chose four fuchsia ones and placed them in the cart then paused in front of a Hello Kitty shower curtain.

I caught my breath, imagining his bachelor pad after his little decorators did their magic.

"Hello Kitty! Look Mom, there's a matching trash can and soap dish, too. Can we get them all?"

I nodded and smiled, a woman confident her Pottery Barn bath sheets were safe and dry on their rack at home. "Kitchen things next!" Shopping always made me feel better and I felt the weight on my heart begin to lift. I pointed to my older daughter. "Your turn. What do you think Daddy would like?"

She picked out a four-place set of forest green dishes with tiny ducks swimming around the rim, matching placemats and a set of utensils that looked like they couldn't cut butter.

"Perfect! Your daddy will love eating his take-out pizza off of these." I looked at my oldest. My son had a better understanding of how our lives would change and my heart ached for him. I took a deep breath. "Now, what about the bedroom?"

We strolled over to the linens. I gazed at the selection of sheets I wouldn't be sleeping on, at the comforters that wouldn't be comforting me.

"That's the one." My son pointed to a display of a Star Wars bed. A full-sized furry Chewbacca lounged on the front of the comforter. Luke Skywalker and Darth Vader battled it out on the sheets. "Look, Mom! Their light sabers glow in the dark!"

As thrilled as I should have been at the prospect of my husband hosting adult slumber parties on Star Wars linens, I felt a twinge of sorrow. I mourned not only the death of my marriage, but the demise of our family unit. I grieved for an entire generation living in a world where happily-ever-after was a fairy tale only half of us could believe.

Maybe I should just let him take whatever he wants. My home will never be the same anyway.

As we were walking to the cash registers, I caught my reflection in a mirror for sale in home goods. I paused to study the broken woman before me, her eyes red and swollen from nights of crying, dark circles pooled under them from lack of sleep. The cheap glass distorted her body, making her look short and squat in her husband's old sweatshirt. I wanted to give her a hug, to reach out to her and tell her everything would be ok, but I wasn't convinced it would be. I reached for the mirror and added it to the pile in the cart.

The kids ran off to look at magazines and I walked to the front of the store to pay, placing our items one by one on the conveyer belt. The cashier, a Barry White double in a blue vest, smiled, the gold on his teeth glinting under the fluorescent lights. He wore a nametag that read, "I'm J.J. Our People Make the Difference." I felt him checking me out before the first item reached his register.

"You're beautiful." His voice was husky as he reached for a pink towel.

I picked up a *National Enquirer* and pretended I didn't hear him. Was this my destiny as a divorced woman, to be at the mercy of every Tom, Dick and J.J.? I imagined the two of us holding hands, taking romantic walks through the produce department after midnight.

He stared into my eyes as he scanned the Hello Kitty soap dish. "You're the most beautiful woman in the whole, wide..."

I caught my breath, not sure whether to be flattered or horrified.

He drew out the next word: "Walmart."

I gave him a half smile and averted my eyes to the woman waiting behind me. She was sporting a home perm and nude leggings one size too friendly and staring at me intently. The pink rhinestone cowboy boots she wore told me this wasn't her first rodeo.

"Honey, you can do better." She winked one blue shadowed eye at me.

J.J. told me I owed him $63.88 and asked for my phone number. I started to say no, then thought better of it and scribbled some numbers on the back of a torn receipt. A smile crept up the corners of my lips as I collected the kids and strolled to the car.

That night my husband came over wearing a sheepish expression, holding empty trash bags. "Just came by to pack up some things."

The kids ran up to greet him with hugs.

"You don't have to pack Daddy," said our youngest. "We bought everything brand new just for you." She pointed to the bundles of blue Walmart bags lined up with love by the front door, a pink towel peeking out of one. "I can't wait to help you decorate our new apartment!"

He caught my eye, raised his eyebrows and nodded in surrender. "How'd I get so lucky?"

I pointed to the mirror we'd bought propped up against the wall. "That's for you, too."

He picked it up and studied his tired, middle-aged reflection in the warped glass, scowled, then tucked the mirror under his arm. He scooped up the bags and was heading to his truck when his cell phone rang and he pulled it out of his pocket.

"Who? J.J.? I don't know any J.J." He juggled the Walmart bags in his arms. "Exactly WHY do you want to talk to my wife?"

A chuckle slipped out of my mouth as I shut the door. Giggles erupted from my throat, then my belly exploded with glee. I laughed until the joyful tears that ran down my face washed away a month's worth of sad ones.

Wiping my eyes, I realized that even though we weren't destined to live happily ever after, we'd be exes for life, bound eternally through the precious children we'd brought into the world. We'd reunite for all the important family milestones, standing side-by-side in silent solidarity, celebrating every graduation and wedding. One day we'd hold newborn grandchildren in our arms, recognizing tiny bits of ourselves in their wrinkled faces. In time we would be friends, and that would last forever.

I wouldn't say I was the happiest woman in the whole world.

However ... I was on my way to becoming the happiest one in Walmart.

Hitting the High Note

Every mother dreads the window of time between 3:00 and 4:00pm. The total opposite of a Happy Hour (which signals the end of a long, hard workday) the Yappy Hour signals the beginning of a long, hard night. It's the dreaded hour in the afternoon when a mother must make the jarring transition from having a small portion of the day to herself to sacrificing every second left of it to her children. This ominous hour is filled with tears (some of them the children's), emotional meltdowns, homework emergencies, and mad dashes to after school activities.

The only cure for the after school yappies was snacks. Lots of them. In an effort to smooth out this particular afternoon, I was in the kitchen wearing my still sweaty work-out clothes, licking brownie batter off a wooden spoon when my daughter, Kati, bounded home from school waving a neon flyer.

"There's going to be a talent show!" She banged a zebra print backpack on the counter and threw open the refrigerator. "I already have my act all planned out." She rummaged around for a Capri Sun, poked the tiny straw into the hole and took a long sip. Her curly, long, brown hair was mussed from the bus ride home. She brushed an impatient hand through it.

"That's great!" I studied my ambitious middle child and grinned. I never had to worry about Kati who made straight As and was a member of the student council. Enrolled in the advancement program at school, she did homework for fun. Everything seemed to come naturally for my daughter. Kati took dance lessons; making it to the coveted front row in the recital each year. "So what are you doing for the show? Ballet? Tap? Jazz?" There was nothing this girl couldn't do.

Kati beamed. "I'm going to sing!"

Except that.

A familiar fear wrapped its fingers around my heart like a vise. "Sing?" I could barely find my voice. "How about a nice little dance? You could get one of your friends to be in your act."

Kati planted both hands on her tiny hips.

"You could recite a poem. You could perform a skit." I broke out into a sweat. "How about a magic show?" With any luck she could make this terrible idea disappear into thin air.

Kati dismissed my suggestions with a wave of her hand. "I'm going to dress up in red, white and blue."

I nodded. "Okay..."

"Then I'm going to sing *The Star-Spangled Banner.*"

I gasped. "Maybe we can find an *easier* tune."

"It has to be *The Star-Spangled Banner.*"

I hid my childhood phobia with a phony laugh. "Only Whitney Houston's ever been able to rock *The Star-Spangled Banner.* Besides, I doubt we can find the music in time."

Kati shook her head. "I don't want music."

My jaw dropped like an opera singer's as she described in frightening detail how she planned to open the show with a star spangled solo of the most difficult song in the world, *a capella*. After her pitch perfect patriotic performance, my little firecracker would break out into a tap dance to the tune of *In the Navy,* which would end with her landing in a split, waving a sparkler and saluting the American flag.

"So what do you think?"

I think I want to throw up. Suddenly I was eleven years old again singing a rousing round of *Row, Row, Row Your Boat* in a stuffy school auditorium. I could hear the laughter of my classmates as my voice and my dreams fell flat at their feet, still taste my first bitter bite of rejection.

Back when I was a young girl, I dreamed of being a singer in a rock & roll band. Every Friday night I watched the Partridge Family and fantasized I was the hip older sister Laurie who managed to be both hot and cool at the same time in groovy 70s clothes. But the real reason I was glued to the TV screen each week was to drool over her brother Keith, the lead singer and my secret heartthrob.

Keith really shook my tambourine when he sang *I Think I Love You.* Whenever I heard that song I was sure there were only two things keeping me from running my fingers through his dark, feathered hair and pursuing a musical career. The first was that my dad, who did not drive a psychedelic school bus or play a musical instrument, forbade me to wear bell-bottom jeans. The second was that I just needed one big break.

Despite these minor details, I held nightly concerts in the privacy of my bathroom where I practiced singing into the steamy mirror, shaking my hips and holding a plastic hairbrush like a microphone. Sometimes David Cassidy made a surprise appearance in the mist beside me and we made beautiful music together, singing in perfect harmony to the beating of my heart. Flinging my wavy, waist length hair and staring soulfully at his reflection, I was sure I had all the right moves for a budding tween star.

So when my 5th grade music teacher announced there would be tryouts for the school chorus, I was the first to sign up. After all that practice, I was sure I'd get one of the lead solos in the Christmas play later that year. With any luck, I would get to stand close to Donny Donaldson, my latest crush, who I felt was the Sutton Elementary School blonde equivalent of David Cassidy.

The morning of the tryouts, Mom drove me to school. My mother, who had heard me belting out *Come on Get Happy* from behind the bathroom door for weeks, let it slip that she wasn't my greatest fan.

"Now, don't feel bad if you don't make it." She gave me a worried look as she pulled up to the curb and handed me my Partridge Family lunchbox. "No one in our family can sing."

It was true. The few times a year we were forced to screech our off-key version of the Happy Birthday song to one of our family members just showcased our lack of talent. It'd be a far happier day for everyone if we'd just mouth the words like we did when we had to sing in church.

But I'd been practicing. Rolling my eyes, I checked my reflection in the visor mirror. For the audition, I'd parted my dark hair in the middle and thought I looked a teensy bit like Susan Dey. "Thanks for the vote of confidence, **Mom**." Bolting from the car, I hurried into school. I was just minutes away from being discovered and didn't want to be late.

In the stuffy auditorium, Mrs. Penny was seated in front of a tired looking upright piano. I joined the group of about thirty 5th graders gathered in a half circle around her and scoped out my competition, zeroing in on a petite blonde girl standing shamelessly close to Donny Donaldson. I squeezed between them and began warming up with the others.

"La, la, *la,* la, laaaaa." I performed with the passion of a pop star.

Mrs. Penny's eyes bulged behind her bifocals. "Again!" Her fingers fluttered over the keyboard.

"La, la, *la,* la, laaaa!" My chest vibrated under my training bra as I vocalized the scale.

Mrs. Penny stopped playing and glared in our direction.

"It wasn't me!" Donny exclaimed in a well-tuned tenor voice.

"Once more!" She pounded on the piano.

"La, la, *la,* la..."

Mrs. Penny focused on me.

"LAAAA!"

She shook her head. My face turned red as I noticed some of the others pointing at me. "Ha, ha, *ha,* ha, haaaa!" they laughed.

The rest of the tryouts were a blur. We progressed to singing *Row, Row, Row Your Boat* over and over again, until Mrs. Penny divided us into tidy little groups. The cute blonde girls with tiny, whiny voices were suddenly sopranos. The boys were tenacious tenors.

"Gently down the stream..." The girls and boys crooned in perfect harmony.

Mrs. Penny eyed the few of us who remained. Left standing beside me was a girl even taller than I was with a mouthful of braces and a boy with a buzz cut. I looked at the teacher expectantly, my heart beating like a metronome in double time. We'd made the cut! I held my breath, imagining the solos she was going to assign to her favored trio.

"Well," she sighed, "we always need stage hands." She turned back to her newly formed chorus who continued to sing merrily.

My heart plummeted. I hung my head and mouthed to my sneakers, "Life is but a dream..."

I never sang in public again. To cap the dream off for good, ABC cancelled the Partridge Family.

That foolish fantasy fizzled, but now, twenty-five years later, my talented in everything but singing daughter was staring up at me, trusting I could make her dream a reality. I squared my shoulders and looked into my daughter's hopeful hazel eyes. "I think we better get busy."

Kati smiled up at me. "I'm going to make my costume right now." She ran towards her room, hair flying. "Oh, say can you SEE..." she screeched.

I winced as she slammed her door. The trouble was, I *could* see. I could hear, too. We were up pitch creek without a piano.

With the talent show less than a week away, and my daughter's self-esteem hanging on a frayed vocal cord, I did what any good mother would do. **I panicked.** Then I did everything in my power to make sure she would win.

We designed a patriotic costume that would make Uncle Sam proud. We choreographed a dance worthy of a Village People music video, but without the pumping pelvises and handle bar moustaches. I was secretly relieved when she refused my help with the singing portion of her act. *That would be like the tone deaf leading the tone deaf.* All I could hope for was that her enthusiasm, big smile and toe tapping talent would dazzle the judges.

The morning of the show I followed Kati, who appeared to have smeared herself in glue and slept in a bed of glitter, into the cafetorium. She disappeared behind the stage while I found a seat with the other mothers. The air was taut; I could feel the tension as the stage moms bragged about their prodigies. While the next Baryshnikov, Pavarotti and Mary Lou Retton were warming up backstage with Kati, I was sweating it out in the audience, distressed over my daughter's debut performance.

A plump woman in khakis, a chambray shirt and sneakers walked out onto the stage and adjusted the mic. She cringed as children of all ages and sizes burst into the room, overjoyed to be out of the classroom for the event. "No Running! Quietly take a seat." Metal chairs clanged as they tripped over each other in their rush to find a place to sit in the audience.

The smell of ripe tuna sandwiches, chalk and playground sweat, combined with that familiar old school smell from my childhood hit me in the face like a dodge ball. The mothers around me glowed in anticipation. They couldn't wait for the show to begin. I couldn't wait for it to be over.

"A very special third grader is opening the show today." Miss Khaki waited for the children to settle down. "Please give a big hand for Kati."

I sat on the edge of my seat, heart pounding, as Kati marched onto the stage and saluted the crowd. Silence thundered as she approached the microphone, put her hand on her heart and tilted her chin. Mothers turned to smile at me. I held my breath until my face turned as red as Kati's sparkly shirt.

"Oh say can you SEE..." Kati bellowed over the speakers. Some of the children held their ears as the sound system screeched, drowning out her words. "By the dawn's early light."

The mothers' faces froze and they examined their manicures. I hunched my shoulders like a humiliated 5th grader and slid down into my seat. The next thirty seconds felt like thirty years.

"And the rockets red..." Kati sang her heart out as a boy in the audience pantomimed an opera singer, arms outstretched, his mouth forming a huge black circle on his face. "GLARE."

Miss Khaki stared daggers at the boy, then turned her attention back to Kati and listened politely. I held my breath. The highest note in the song was seconds away.

"O'er the laa-and of the..." Kati scrunched up her face and sang like her brother had just snatched the last chocolate chip cookie. "FREEEEE!"

The word gave me goosebumps as it rang through the room like a fire alarm, waking something up deep inside me. I *was* free. *We* were free. Free to try new things, even if we didn't excel at them. Free to speak our words, *sing* our words, use our voices, even if they weren't perfect.

The next thing I knew, as if the spirit of David Cassidy had reached down through my mist-filled memories and plucked me out of my seat, I was suddenly on my feet, standing in the middle of the crowded cafetorium. I beamed at my daughter in admiration. She smiled and drew a deep, dramatic breath.

"And the home of the..." Kati warbled.

My little girl, you're so... I felt the little voice inside me that had been shamed into silence stir back to life.

"BRAVE!" Kati and I sang in unison (if not harmony) the spirit of David Cassidy singing an enthusiastic background vocal from the rafters above.

A stunned silence followed.

"My brave baby girl," I whispered towards the stage, then, noticing the moms looking up at me, mouths gaping open, quickly slid back into my seat.

Miss Khaki clapped three times slowly while someone figured out how to work the sound system. Seconds later, *In the Navy* stormed the school. Kati didn't miss a beat as she tapped and shuffled across the slick stage floor, saluting her classmates and working them up into a military mania.

"We want you! We want you!" The audience sang along to the song, pointing to Kati as she sashayed and shimmied and shook the room. My heart leaped with hope. But in the end, what they really wanted was a shaggy haired boy who could walk the dog with a neon yellow yo-yo.

"I thought he was pretty good." Kati seemed unconcerned as she fiddled with the stereo button in the car on the way home from the school.

"*Phhht.*" I could barely hide my disappointment and disgust. It would take more than homemade brownies this afternoon to make me feel better.

The CD player spit a well-worn compact disc into her hand. "What the heck is this?" She squinted at the disc and sneered, "The *Partridge* Family?"

I felt my face flush. "It's nothing! Put it back."

"Is that a *school* bus on the CD?" She slid the disc into the player and turned up the volume.

A tune as familiar as an old friend blasted from the speakers. My schoolgirl crush crooned for us to get happy, and in spite of the dismal day, a smile crossed my face. Suddenly I was back in the bathroom of my youth, singing into a steamy mirror, a whole lifetime of lessons before me. My fingers tapped the steering wheel to the beat.

I glanced at my daughter humming beside me, no doubt dreaming of her next challenge, the rejection of the day already a distant memory.

Rolling down the windows, I felt the rush of the wind as it blew back my hair, taking my breath away, but not my newfound voice.

"Come on, get happy!" I sang off-key at the top of my lungs. Kati joined in, using her flip flop as a makeshift microphone. We sang all the way home, loudly and out of tune, two women who had found their voices and weren't afraid to use them.

At least in the privacy of their own car.

Spin Cycle

I survived my last birthday, even learning to live with the pile of unwelcome gifts from Mother Nature, including roots that give *Fifty Shades of Grey* new meaning. Some of Her presents were as subtle as sweat in the middle of winter and as tiny as the cluster of smile lines barely visible without reading glasses. She even sent me a greeting card in the mail in the form of an AARP membership offer which fluttered to the bottom of the trash with the other junk mail.

She also blessed me with saddlebags full of cellulite and a healthy dose of absent-mindedness, which I promptly forgot all about. Last, she plucked all the filters off me, one by one, like coarse white chin hairs, until I shocked even myself by what I'd say and do.

"How'd you like to teach our spinning class tomorrow?" the manager of Bally Fitness said, catching me on the way to Zumba evening class. "I just lost my instructor and I've seen you take the class." He eyed me warily. "Unless it would be too much for you..."

"Sure!" my 20-something mind answered, flattered. "I've been taking the class for years." *Are you crazy?* My 50-nothing body argued back. *You weigh more than you did nine months pregnant, and you'll have to wear spandex. In a mirrored room!*

The next day, armed with an iPod of 80s hits and a sense of false bravado, I sucked in my stomach and entered the spinning room, smiling confidently at the class already seated on the fourteen spin cycles facing the mirrored wall.

"Where's Veronica?" A blonde with bee stung lips in a pumped-up jog bra gave me the once over.

I plugged in my iPod and climbed onto my bike facing the class, trying to ignore the fact that my spandexed bottom was on display from every conceivable angle in the mirrored room. *I Will Survive* bellowed from the speakers as I began to pedal as if what was left of my life depended on it.

A bored looking young man flexed a bicep as he glanced at his watch. I turned up the volume and pedaled faster. The blonde rolled her eyes. It was then I remembered another advantage of growing older: you don't care what people think anymore.

Unless they think you're old.

"She's old enough to be my mother," the fit man said, laughed and nudged the blonde.

I'll show you a mother! I made it my personal goal to wipe that smirk off the man's face. This was war, and it would not end until the blonde's sweat was pooled in a puddle at her feet and her boyfriend begged for mercy.

Faster and faster I pedaled, cuing the class through standing climbs and jumps. I was a vision in the mirror, a crazed woman with a halo of hair frizzing around my face, one lone gray hair standing defiantly like a diamond studded exclamation point at the top of my head.

My varicose vein pulsed to the beat of the music.

Old enough to be your mother! What a load of bull...

"Sprint!" I demanded. "Faster!"

It was then I noticed an older gentleman at the back of the class. He met my gaze and smiled, fanning himself with his hand. If I could have caught my breath, I would have breathed a sigh of relief. *Positive feedback!* The next song was by ABBA. *Take a Chance on Me* came on and to my surprise, he pointed to his chest, clearly moved by the words. Flushed, I looked away.

It had been several years since my divorce. I had devoted myself to my children which gave me little time to meet new men. I peeked back at him. He pantomimed holding a drink, bringing it to his lips, suggestively. I glanced away, embarrassed at the attention. I was a professional. It would be inappropriate for me to meet with a student out of class. His desire was unmistakable. I led the class through a grueling series of jumps, lost in thought.

I'd always pictured myself with someone closer to my age. If I squinted, he resembled the Dos Equis man, that distinguished bearded model on the beer commercials. I don't date men from the gym often, but when I do, it's...

Dose of your own medicine, that's what you need! I glared at the fit young man and the blonde in the front row. *I might be old, but I'm not dead, and I'm not going to let this opportunity flash by me.*

I began the cool down, looking back at my admirer. He winked at me, tugged at his shirt collar, and raised his hand to his mouth in a drinking motion. As the last song ended, he hugged the handlebars of his bike, a man spent and satisfied, soon to be hungering for more.

Yes! I smiled triumphantly and hopped off my bike. *I'll meet you after class for a drink. I'll ride off into the sunset with you. I'll be yours forever, my knight in shining Under Armor.*

I started for the door.

"That was a killer class!" The fit man's mouth hung open in surprise. I stopped long enough to gloat as the blonde beside him swiped at the rivulets of black mascara crying down from her Botoxed brow. "That old dude's barely moving."

I hurried to the locker room to freshen up before happy hour with my new friend.

Minutes later, I floated back into the gym in a cloud of Cavalli and waited expectantly for my date. *He's probably a retired millionaire who'll beg me to travel the world with him.* Deep in thought, I almost didn't hear the wail of the ambulance outside.

"Where have you been?" my manager growled running up to me, scowling.

"I was changing. I had the best class! Everyone loved me. Well, some more than others, obviously." I glanced around for my date. If he stood me up, he was a dead man.

"You're fired!" he shouted at me. "Didn't you see that old man in your class? He collapsed! Some blonde told me he was trying to get your attention. We called an ambulance!"

"That's impossible!" my 20-something mind argued. I clutched my mouth as the paramedics wheeled my ashen admirer out of the spin room. He winced when he saw me and weakly flipped his middle finger, a last defiant gesture.

The nerve of him! my 50-nothing body protested. *If he thinks I'm going to nurse him back to health, he's got another thing coming.* I turned my spandexed back to him and strode out of the gym. Dating was like riding a bike. All I had to do was hop back on and it would all come back to me.

And thankfully, by tomorrow, my aging mind would let me forget my broken heart.

Tongue-Tied

For months after my divorce, each night after my children went to bed I locked myself in the bedroom of my broken home and cried myself to sleep. Crushed and humiliated, I missed my marriage, my happy family unit, my once perfect life. I allowed my shattered soul to mourn.

Then I went out, bought some new underwear, and joined an online dating website.

I drooled over the endless possibilities the internet had to offer a newly divorced woman. I explored single parent sites. Hot, shirtless dads cradled babies against their bare chests. *Father of six seeks soccer mom to share game nights and diaper duty.* I scrolled through silver single sites. *Sexy senior octogenarian seeks fun forty-something to share sponge baths and overnight homecare.*

I was about to give up when one site caught my eye. *Find the agape of your life on GreekFriends.com!* On the home page, gorgeous Greek men holding platters of skewered meat smiled seductively in front of whitewashed villas. I could almost hear the bouzouki music of my ancestors playing in the background. I imagined my Greek dad nodding in approval.

Taking a deep breath, I logged in and met the first hopeful: an engineer from Houston named George. *Strong, silent type seeks demure, petite blonde to share quiet dinners.* I fluffed my long brown hair and stretched my statuesque frame. *Who cares what* he *wants?* George hadn't posted a photo, but I envisioned tall and manly, a Sam Elliott type, rugged and reserved, confident, sexy. "This one's for you, Dad," I whispered to the screen.

One week later, after a flurry of flirty instant messages, I walked into the Olive Garden to meet the man of my dreams.

I searched the crowd for a Greek version of Sam Elliot who would sweep me off my feet and onto the first plane for Mykonos. My gaze settled on an unassuming man of medium height with dark hair standing alone by a potted plant. My heart sank. The only things visibly strong about him were his black, bushy eyebrows, two caterpillars mating on his face. Clearly my hairy godmother misunderstood my request.

Instead of Sam Elliott, she sent me Yosemite Sam.

I gave him a weak smile and held out my hand. "You must be George."

The caterpillars jumped up on his forehead, then drew together, huddled in disappointment as he scowled up at me. He offered me a sweaty hand and a curt nod. I sized him up as the hostess led us to a cozy booth by the kitchen. George had claimed to be taller than average on his profile. This was true only if the common height of an American male was 5'2".

At first the waiter talked for us. He announced the specials and asked easy questions. Would we like lemon with our water? Would we like to see a menu? We nodded in unison. He retreated to the kitchen and a suffocating cloud of silence descended on our table.

I took a deep breath and gave George my most engaging smile. He flinched and studied his menu, the caterpillars connecting in concentration.

"So, what's good here?" I asked with my eyes glued to his brows. They were so mesmerizing I gave them names. Harry and Forrest.

He continued to browse the menu, then pointed to a picture of a pasta dish right as the waiter reappeared to take our order.

"Excellent choice," he said to my date. He looked at me, pad posed.

I attempted to send him a telepathic message. *Help me!* I pleaded silently, looking deep into his eyes. *I'm on my first date in twenty years and I'm beginning to believe I wore Spanx for nothing.* I contemplated spelling out SOS with breadcrumbs on my placemat.

"Chicken," I said, more to myself than the waiter. "Chicken *Afraid*-o. And a bottle of wine."

"Certainly. White? Red?" He looked at George. "Do you prefer a full body?" There was only silence.

"This is our first date." I took a huge gulp of lemon water. "I don't know what type of body he prefers."

Harry and Forest leaped into George's hairline, clearly shocked. Then the four of us settled back into an uncomfortable silence.

We were twenty minutes into lunch when I suspected my blind date might also be mute. Amazingly, George still hadn't uttered one word. It was so quiet at our table I could hear our lettuce wilting. If he'd been a shade paler and shown up wearing a beret, customers might have mistaken him for a mime.

The waiter served our food. I peeked up at George over my barely touched meal and admired his hearty appetite. Twirl. Chew. Swallow. With the precision of an engineer, he focused on twisting his spaghetti onto his fork. Perhaps he was too polite to talk with his mouth full.

So I talked. I tried bonding with him over our common background and gave an animated monologue about growing up Greek. Back in the day, we wouldn't have met at Olive Garden, I gushed. He would have picked me up and my father would have met him at the door, his muscles bulging out of his undershirt, rifle in hand.

Harry and Forrest looked up at me in horror. "Shhh," they seemed to say. "Can't you see we're eating?"

When George didn't actually respond, I asked questions, instead. Was he a sports enthusiast? *Maybe he'd lost his voice cheering on his favorite team.* Did he have pets? *Maybe his cat had got his tongue.*

Nothing. My shoulders slumped in defeat. And why didn't he have questions for me? *Aren't you curious, George?*

This date was a Greek tragedy. I'd just decided to hurl myself off a mountain of pasta and end it all when the waiter brought the check and saved me from my fate.

I reached for my purse, mentally calculating what half of horrible came out to, plus tip. But George sent me a warning look, shooting Harry up into his hairline while Forrest burrowed down close to one eye. Browbeaten, I allowed him to pay the bill. With a buy one, get one free coupon.

We walked in silence to the parking lot. I couldn't wait to go home to my children who had no problem talking back to me.

I spotted my car and half jogged to where I was parked, George hot on my tail. There would be no awkward pauses, no long goodbyes. I would leap into my car and speed away, leaving his furry little face forever.

My hand was reaching for the car door when I felt the tip of his finger on my waist. I turned to face him. The caterpillars gazed at me like I was a tasty leaf they couldn't wait to munch. *Surely he doesn't expect a kiss!*

To my surprise, in a deep, resonant voice that would put Barry White to shame, he announced his first words of the date. "Can I call you?" His eyebrows may have screamed Yosemite Sam, but in that shocking moment, his velvety voice was pure Elliott.

For the first time that day, I was speechless. Then I said the one thing I knew to guarantee I would never hear from him again. "Shhh-ure."

He swaggered off to his car.

I knew he wouldn't call me and he knew I wouldn't answer if he did, but in the dating world, some things are better left unsaid.

Just ask George.

Juan, Two, Three

When my husband left me for a sexy one-bedroom midtown apartment and a racy two-seater convertible, I wanted revenge.

Nothing would have made me happier at that moment than swinging my son's official Little League baseball bat at the contrite expression on his apologetic face. Stuck with a five-bedroom home in the suburbs of Houston, three children under the age of twelve, and a soccer mom Suburban, I agonized over my broken family and shattered dreams. My future seemed as bright as the shallow cut half-carat I slipped off my finger and into a dresser drawer.

But what I worried most about being a single mom was that my children would be cheated out of family vacations. It was hard enough juggling their daily routines when I was married. Two parents trying to tackle school, homework, and extracurricular activities for three children was challenging, almost impossible if one parent considered his share completed by shouting encouragement from a spot on the sofa in front of the TV.

After my divorce, traveling alone with three children across *town* was daunting enough. Traveling with them out of the country could prove to be the surest way to give a newly liberated mother a one-way ticket to a nervous breakdown.

Yet I was freshly divorced; fueled by anger and self-righteousness. I longed for white beaches and tropical drinks and for my children to believe their mom was superwoman disguised in denim shorts and silver bangles. Warm and sunny was what we all needed after a dark year.

I went to a travel agency and purchased four tickets to Cancun. Then I checked our passports, flipping them open one by one to make sure none had expired.

I examined my own photo first. Taken when I was still a blissful bride, my hair hung in soft brown waves past my shoulders. My younger self gazed into the camera with an open, unguarded smile, a woman who was confident her husband loved her no matter how unflattering her passport picture, a woman trusting the future held exotic destinations and happy times ahead.

I opened Alston's next. He grinned back at me from the tiny postage stamp size photo. Athletic and witty, and a little reserved, he already towered over me. I could always count on my oldest to add teenage humor to any situation. My middle child's passport was next. Kati with her curly hair was serious and smart, always challenging herself to excel, and even at the age of eleven she was willing to mother the rest of us with her worldly advice. I opened Kristina's book last and smiled when I saw her wide, brown eyes staring back at me from behind a pair of glasses. Thin and delicate, with long brown hair that never seemed brushed, my sensitive, but outspoken youngest child worried over our family like a Greek grandmother in an eight-year-old body.

I hugged the blue leather passports to my chest and took a deep breath. To me they symbolized freedom. I was eager to prove to everyone, especially myself, our adventures were just beginning.

I broke the news to my mother first.

"Are you sure?" my mother asked in a worried voice when she found out I was taking her precious grandchildren to a foreign country. "There are drug wars there. Why don't you just borrow the beach house for the week if you want to get away? There's a lot to do in Galveston."

Then I told my ex-husband.

"Do you really think that's a good idea?" His passive-aggressive tactics no longer had an effect on me. "Don't I have to give you permission to take them out of the country?"

Their lack of confidence in me was the motivation I needed to get us packed and boarded on the plane. When we arrived at our palatial resort and the children's eyes lit up as they spotted the lovely pool, I knew I'd made the right decision. What could possibly go wrong?

We wouldn't spend all week by the pool, I vowed. That was a safe, married thing to do. I directed us to the excursion desk. We must immerse ourselves in the culture and embrace the customs of the country.

"Welcome!" a tan woman with glossy black hair in a pink sun dress greeted us with a blinding smile. She smelled of sunshine and coconuts. "What a beautiful family. How can I help you?"

One look at her and I wished I'd packed one of those Miracle bathing suits guaranteed to make the wearer look ten pounds lighter in ten seconds. I leafed through a colorful binder on her desk. "I'd like to book an excursion for my children and me."

"Of course! I can help you." She looked over my shoulder expectantly. "Should we wait for your husband?"

"Excuse me?" I'd been waiting on him for the last fourteen years.

My son stared at her, his mouth hanging open. "She kind of looks like that actress Dad likes on Modern Family," he said under his breath.

"She's beautiful," Kristina whispered. Her brown eyes widened. "Like one of my Barbie dolls."

Kati wrinkled her nose.

The woman pursed plump pouty lips. "I'd like to talk to both you and your husband," she persisted, her tone growing an edge.

I narrowed my eyes. *And I'm sure he'd like to talk to you.* "Why?" I thrust my chin up in defiance and it quivered a little. *Tell her. Just admit to Miss Mexico your husband was the one piece of baggage you left at home. Why can't you say the D word?*

D-umped.   D-itched.   D-ivorced.

Miss Mexico continued, "I want to let both of you know about the amazing opportunities here to own a condo of your own." She looked annoyed, like a man-less female had never dared approach her desk.

"No husband." I looked her in the eye and dared her to dismiss me. I watched her eyes dull and her chest heave as a huge sigh escaped her lips. "Don't be sad," I said, shrugging and lying just a little. "I'm not."

With a forced smile she recited a memorized list of the excursions then glanced at her watch. I slapped my VISA in her hand and purchased four tickets to Chichen Itza for the next morning.

Enjoy an unforgettable excursion back into the times of the Mayan empire, the brochure promised. *Ride in comfort in an air-conditioned bus!* I hesitated. It had been years since I'd ridden in a bus. I flashed back to a youth group trip I'd taken as a young girl to Wyoming when the altitude and winding roads and a cute boy from Dallas made me weak in my knees. But I was stronger now. I'd stomached heartbreak and a hearty helping of humble pie in the past year. A two-hour bus ride would be a piece of *tres leches. Stop for an authentic buffet lunch in a scenic town on the way to one of the Seven Wonders of the World.* I smiled. My husband would have hated it.

Perfect.

We spent the afternoon at the hotel beach, swimming in the tranquil turquoise sea. The girls got their hair braided by an old woman selling scarves and trinkets, and the kids and I sipped frozen drinks out of coconuts, mine doused with a healthy shot of rum. I settled onto a plush chaise lounge and smiled. Wiggling my toes, I watched the fine white sand sift through them and finally felt myself relax. I may no longer be a good wife (that wasn't my fault) but I was still a good mother.

The wakeup call came too early the next morning. I dragged the kids out of bed, sprayed them with Coppertone and filled my backpack with essentials for the day. Dramamine for carsickness, snacks and Gatorade— no way we were drinking the water here— money and a credit card. When we boarded the bus on time and settled into the first two rows, I took a deep breath of the stale air and smiled at the children, certain we were prepared for anything. Nothing bad would happen to these kids while Supermom was in charge.

A smooth-talking tour guide with dark wavy hair welcomed us. Juan, a self-professed expert in Mayan history and culture, would accompany us to lunch, lead us through the ruins, then bring us back to our hotel in time for dinner.

"We have such an exciting fun day planned," Juan's Spanish-tinged accent was amplified through the poor-quality microphone he held. "Unless, of course, you're a virgin." His eyes scanned the bus and settled on a curvy teen sitting next to her mother. "The Mayan priests in the Yucatan sacrificed virgins by throwing them into sinkholes, *cenotes*, to petition the gods for rain and fertile fields."

Kati blushed.

"I hope *you're* not a virgin, Mom!" Kristina drew closer to me, her beaded braids pressed against my chest.

Juan raised his bushy eyebrows up and down. "Best *not* to be a virgin for too long in the Mayan culture."

Alston scrunched up his face. "Yuck-atan."

"You'll be happy to know our bus has a restroom." Juan gestured to the back. "But it's a Mexican restroom, not an American restroom." He waited for us to stop wondering out loud. "This means if you have to go number one, no *problema*. If you have to go number two..." he held his nose and fanned his face, "raise your hand like this." He raised his arm and made the peace sign with his fingers. "And that will be the signal for me to tell the driver to pull over at the nearest rest stop for you to do your business." His tone grew more serious, "We're not equipped to handle *numero dos. Comprende?*"

I gasped. I couldn't imagine what kind of person would actually notify the entire bus they had to have a bowel movement, much less force everyone to pull over while they did the deed. I rolled my eyes. Only in Mexico!

The kids dozed off during Juan's lecture. He explained Chichen Itza means the mouth at the well of Itza. The huge area composed of architectural wonders contains a temple and an ancient playing field. After an especially dramatic description of the mystical powers of the pyramids, Juan shut off his microphone and ambled down the aisle, pausing to laugh and joke along the way. He stopped by my seat, glanced at my sleeping children, then reverted his eyes back to me, allowing them to linger on the collar of my embroidered blouse. "Your husband doesn't want to explore the pyramids?" He flashed a brilliant smile.

"Not these, anyway," I shot back, then remembered my children were in hearing range and pressed my lips together grimly.

He raised his eyebrows and stared at me a second too long, then made his way further down the aisle. I cringed at the unwelcome attention. An hour later we pulled up outside of a tired looking hotel in the middle of nowhere.

"And now let's break for a delicious authentic Yucatan meal." Juan stood by the driver as we exited the bus. "All you can eat!"

I herded the kids together. "Remember, don't drink the water." The last thing we needed on this trip was a family epidemic of Montezuma's Revenge. We walked up to an unimpressive buffet line. The kids examined the selection and hesitantly picked up plates.

"My, oh Maya!" Alston held up a soggy sausage with a pair of tongs. "This looks good."

I slapped the sausage out of his hand. "No pork! I Googled it. Undercooked pork is a recipe for disaster. Try rice, beans, tortillas." I examined each item they put on their plates like an FDA inspector. "No fresh fruit or salad." I speared a piece of chicken with a serving fork and placed it on my plate next to a portion of fish smothered in sauce. "And don't drink the water!" We sat at a long table and the kids picked at their food. Too chicken to eat much chicken, I nibbled at the lukewarm fish, changed my mind and spooned some refried beans into my mouth.

Juan sauntered up to our table and glanced at my half-eaten plate. "Are you enjoying the carnitas?"

"No carnitas for me. Just a little chicken."

"No mama, that's carnitas." Juan smirked at the expression on my face. "Pork. Mexican style."

I *thought* it had looked a little gray. Trying to hide the worry from my face, I gathered the children up and we followed the others back onto the bus. Juan played Mariachi music from an eight-track tape player all the way to the ruins. My tummy rumbled to the festive beat.

We filed off the bus and followed Juan to the entrance. He chattered happily, pointing out the information desk and restrooms, then slowed down to walk by my side.

He tapped my arm to get my attention and pointed to an ambulance parked by the gate. "That's in case someone gets sick." His expression grew ominous and he continued in a singsong voice, "You never know." A chill ran up my spine despite the hot tropical sun. He nodded, then hurried off to the front of the line to lead our group on a tour of the grounds.

An angry sun glared down directly into my eyes. Humidity weighed heavily on my shoulders and within minutes I was drenched with sweat. My legs felt heavy and I seemed to be moving in slow motion as I struggled to keep up with the others.

Alston saw I was lagging behind and slowed down to wait for me. "Hurry up, Mom! We're going to see the Great Ball Court." He allowed me to clutch his arm. "Juan says if you clap at one end of the field, it will produce nine echoes at the center." He felt the clamminess of my hand against his skin and studied my face. "You don't look so good."

"I'm feeling a little dizzy. The heat..." I felt weak. My legs were shaking by the time we made it to the court where Juan was demonstrating how sound carried by clapping his hands sharply while the others listened half a football field away. I clung onto Alston for support, waiting for Juan to finish his explanation so I could to ask him where I could find a spot to sit in the shade until I felt better. My stomach bloated over my waistband and I undid the button of my jeans.

Juan clapped again for the group and they clapped back nine times in response, in awe of the acoustics of the court. He noticed me standing beside him in the silent moment that followed and his eyes lit up. I could smell his aftershave as he leaned in to whisper something in my ear, but before the first flirtatious comment could escape his lips, my body made a noise of its own, sending him reeling away in disgust.

"Mom!" Alston's mouth hung open in teenage admiration.

The explosive clap from my bowels ripped across the court, nine sharp blasts resonating in the middle where the tour group huddled. They laughed and cheered in response, then blew nine ripe raspberries back at us. Juan glared at me. Seconds away from having the runs at the ruins, I clutched my stomach and hobbled, doubled over to the restroom by the entrance. Agonizing cramps seared through my body as I waited in line to use the tiny facilities. I contemplated finding the closest sinkhole and sacrificing myself to the gods, but given my marital history, I was sure I'd be spewed out in exchange for the nearest virgin.

As I inched my way closer to the front, I realized with horror an old woman dressed all in black was rationing out squares of toilet paper. One, two, three squares each, every woman in line was allocated the same amount. When I reached her, she distributed three sheets of the rough, thin tissue to me, took one look at my sweaty face, and handed me one more. I stayed holed up in the steamy stall until Kati and Kristina wandered in an hour later frantically calling my name.

Somehow they loaded me on the bus and sat me in the aisle seat next to Kristina. "I wish Dad were here," she whimpered. She fanned me with a map of Chichen Itza while Kati gave me small sips of water from a bottle.

For an agonizing hour, I concentrated on clenching, begging my bowels to respect the rules of the bus and remain calm on the long trip to the resort. Somehow, I made it half way back to Cancun. Then without warning and without raising my hand, I leaped from my seat and sprinted down the aisle to the back of the bus. I did number one and number two and what must have been number three in the tiny restroom, fearing the whole time how the Mexican plumbing would react to my insubordination.

No Juan must know!

I considered my options. If I extended my stay in the steamy potty, it would raise suspicion. But if I exited, I feared what repercussions awaited me on the other side of the door. I slapped cold water on my face, gearing up for my walk of shame. I'd traumatized my children and made a mess of this trip, this tour, and my life. The least I could have done was raise my hand to warn the innocent bystanders.

I cracked open the door expecting to find a sea of Shit-chen Itza flowing down the aisle. But miraculously, the floor was bare. A few passengers had even managed to sleep through my eruption. Juan stared at me warily as I returned to my seat and collapsed beside Kristina. I knew I could count on my youngest for sympathy and a loving hand to hold. She took one look at me and edged closer to the window. "You look green." She shuddered. "And you smell funny."

I mustered up the last of my strength to scavenge through my backpack digging out a half-filled lukewarm Gatorade. I took a few tiny sips of the tepid liquid and cradled the bottle all the way back to the hotel.

When the bus jerked to a stop outside our hotel, I was the first out the door, my kids following close behind me. So thankful to be off the bumpy bus and near a real working toilet, I almost kissed the ground. I shoved some crumpled bills into the tour guide's outstretched palm.

Juan shook my hand and held it a moment too long. "Tell your husband he missed out."

I stared back at him. "He already knows."

Then the bus ride and the undercooked pork and the past year of my life gurgled out of my stomach and up my throat and I raced through the lobby to the ladies room.

Miss Mexico found me hugging the toilet, my cheek pressed against the cool porcelain. "I gave your children some ice cream." She handed me a wet paper towel under the stall.

"Thanks," I mumbled weakly and unlocked the door. I joined her in front of the mirrors and examined my disheveled appearance. Mascara ran down my face. The front of my shirt was stained with something the color of refried beans. In comparison, Miss Mexico looked like she was seconds away from accepting her crown.

She reached into her roomy handbag and pulled out a shot glass. "This is for you."

I shook my head. Alcohol was the last thing I needed. What was wrong with this crazy lady? And what was wrong with me for thinking I could do this alone? She pulled out a shaker of salt and a lime wedge and placed them on the sink. The thought of tequila almost sent me reeling back to the stall. "Thanks, but no thanks. Really."

She reached in a third time and pulled out a bottle of Imodium and waved it in the air. "Ancient Mexican remedy." She poured a long shot into the tiny glass. "From Walmart." Then she sprinkled my palm with salt. She waited while I licked my hand, swallowed the shot and sucked on the tart wedge of lime.

I felt better.

"Not many women are brave enough to travel alone with their children." She nodded her head at my reflection. "But you're giving them the gift of seeing the world."

I smiled feebly.

"Sometimes it's an imperfect world, no? But they'll always remember you traveled it together."

I really felt better now. Miss Mexico's acceptance speech was just the cure I needed. I looked at the younger woman with new eyes. "How'd you get so wise?"

Her lips curled into a sad smile. "You're not the only person who's ever had a broken heart."

We walked back out into the lobby together. The children were huddled around the excursion desk, half-eaten ice cream cones in their hands, pouring over the daily tour binder. My heart swelled at the sight of them. In that instant I realized I may no longer be married, but this handful of happily ever after was all mine. Until death do us part.

"Look, Mom!" Kati pointed to a picture of a tropical paradise. "Visit Xel-Ha aquatic theme park!" she read. "Satisfy your appetite for family fun and adventure. Snorkeling, zip lining, and all you can eat at our international buffet."

I looked at Miss Mexico with alarm. "Don't worry," my new friend said. "We can pack you a lunch. And it's a short taxi ride away."

I raised one hand in the air, two fingers making the victory sign, slapped my VISA in her outstretched palm with the other, and hurried back to the bathroom. I still wasn't 100% but I was getting there. In the meantime, there was a whole world to explore and I wouldn't settle for just any Juan along the way. My kids had bounced back and so would I.

That was the greatest revenge of all.

First Dance

I plastered a smile on my face as the happy couple got into my car and settled themselves comfortably, too comfortably I feared, into the back seat. *His name is Kole. His name is Kole,* I repeated to myself.

Kole, Kole, Kole, I insisted under my breath, vowing not to mispronounce his name again. I glanced at him in the rearview mirror. He looked nice enough, all-American, with a shock of brown hair and freckle-splattered cheeks. I caught a whiff of cologne, certainly not aftershave, his face more boy than man. I smiled smugly. I could take him down. If necessary, one well-aimed bump of my hip could bring him to his knees. I examined his slight build and corrected myself. Physical violence would not be necessary. My purse could flatten him, both straps tied behind its back.

You see...I knew him. As soon as Kati uttered his name months ago with her petal pink lips, the research began. All it took was a few phone calls to a couple of well-connected mothers, and I was armed with his life history. I knew all about him, but he didn't know me.

I am Greek! I wanted to scream and shock that confident smirk off his face. *We make soup out of testicles and serve it to our families at Easter!* I shuddered, recalling how my own father would make an elaborate show of pulling his guns out of a gleaming glass case he kept in the living room when a non-Greek boy would have the audacity to come to the house to pick me up for a date. One by one he would lovingly polish each gun with a rag, his white undershirt stained with sweat. As a result, I had many first dates in high school, but never a second.

Where was my dad when I needed him? As a single mom, I appeared chic and trendy. I baked cookies and served brownies and joked. But inside I seethed and plotted. If only the poor boy could read the thoughts behind my carefully made-up face he would flee from the car, race to the safety of the school and not look back.

It started off innocently enough.

"There's someone I want you to meet." My precious 15-year-old daughter inhaled deeply and sighed. "Kole."

"Coal?" The name tasted bitter on my tongue. Like a piece of carbon Santa brings a bad boy for Christmas. For a moment I allowed myself to fantasize a Kosta had appeared in my daughter's life. That would have pleased her grandfather.

"Cole with a K," she spelled sweetly, dreamily. "K-O-L-E."

"Kole. Oh..." I corrected myself, hearing my father's heavy accent in my mind. "Like the Greek word *kolo*, the body part you sit on."

And so it started. She thought he was perfect, Kole with a K, an aspiring saxophone player in the high school band, and I just thought he was one letter away from being an ass.

"I really like him Mom," she continued ignoring my tone. "We're going out."

"And just where do you think you're *going*?" I knew my daughter's whereabouts twenty-four hours a day: school, church, basketball practice, in her room doing her homework, never remotely near anyone named Kole, or his *kolo*.

Her eyes rolled. "We talk. We text. We sit together at lunch," she continued slowly, as if explaining a difficult concept to a two-year-old. "Everyone knows we like each other."

I breathed a sigh of relief. A crush! Puppy love. Nothing would ever come of this.

"He wants to take me to…"

"No."

"You didn't let me finish."

I wielded my index finger like it was a weapon. "Not until you're sixteen."

We ended up compromising. They were going out without going anywhere, so I pretended that was acceptable to me.

I made a few attempts at being a modern mom despite my old-world upbringing. I picked him up occasionally so they could study at Starbucks, two huge backpacks resting between them in the backseat, an impervious fortress. Months passed…then…the inevitable happened. She turned sixteen!

Outwardly, I celebrated. I threw a huge party for her and thirty of her closest girlfriends and showered her with gifts. Inwardly, I wailed. I tore at my hair and cursed my predicament.

She cornered me the very day after her party. "There's a dance." She took a deep breath. "I want to go with Kole."

"No." My answer was reflexive, as if someone had knocked my knee with a tiny steel hammer.

"But you promised! I'm sixteen. I'll be getting my driver's license soon."

"No," I insisted, yet I felt my resolve to overprotect her melting under the sunny sparkle in her eyes. Her excitement was contagious and I couldn't help but remember being young and in love, bursting with anticipation, glowing with the warmth of a new romance. I scrutinized the mature, responsible young woman before me and fought the urge to be like my father.

Well, that was how I found myself in this predicament, driving this car, one eye on the road and one focused in the rearview mirror, spying on the young couple huddled together in the backseat, sitting shamelessly close, thighs touching, when it was obvious there was enough room for three full-sized strangers to spread out. I cleared my throat loudly, making them jump. "How was the dance?"

"Oh, it was so much fun!" my daughter gushed. "We danced all night. The band was great. Everyone loved my dress."

I watched her in the rearview mirror tug self-consciously at the bodice of her first strapless gown. Kole loosened his bowtie. The hairs on the back of my neck sprang to attention. Something wasn't right. I changed lanes unnecessarily so I would have an excuse to look over my shoulder into the dark back seat.

It was then I saw it. His hand rested ever so lightly on my daughter's pearly white, perfectly shaped knee. *That's my knee!* I wanted to shriek. *I gave birth to that knee! Get your grubby little hand off my perfect little knee or I'll show you what a knee's good for, you little...* I calculated in my mind ... fifteen minutes, twelve if I sped home. Twelve minutes of his feeling up my daughter's knee. Rage blinded me as I fought the urge to pull over, drag him from the car by the neck of his shirt and kick him in the *kolo*.

I talked to distract them: death, war, the famine in Haiti, the earthquake in Chile. If only I could keep his dirty little mind, if not his hand, off my daughter's knee. I glanced at the clock glowing on the dashboard. We had more than a ten-minute drive to Kole's house when the crisis hit. My daughter rested her beautiful head of curls on Kole's shoulder, and closed her eyes.

"Look out!" I screamed, swerving the car violently. Her head flew left, then right from the sudden motion.

"Mom! What the...?"

"A dog!" I lied. "I almost hit a dog! Whew, what a close call. Could you imagine Kole scooping up that poor little poodle? He'd be ringing doorbells all night in his tuxedo, trying to find the owners."

I turned on the radio to a Christian station and raised the volume to gospel proportions. I peeked at them in the rearview mirror as a chorus of nuns sang the Lord's Prayer in soprano. Minutes ticked by. I had just turned onto Kole's street when I saw him swivel his shoulders towards her, leaning closer, his full, pursed lips hovering dangerously over her glossy, vanilla flavored ones.

Without thinking, I jammed on the brakes in the middle of the dark road. *This one's for you, Dad!* I cackled to myself as the car screeched to a stop.

"Ow!" Kole cried as his head snapped forward, then backwards from the sudden halt. He clutched the base of his neck as the pungent aroma of burned rubber filled the car.

"Kole, are you ok?" My daughter grabbed her date's arm then leaned her head over the seat and hissed at me, "Mom, what's wrong with you?"

"Cat! Didn't you see that black cat in the middle of the road?" I fibbed with conviction. "The only thing worse than having a black cat cross in front of you is hitting one. We all would have had bad luck!" I quickly pulled up in front of Kole's house, parked the car and snapped on the interior lights.

"Thank you for the ride," Kole oozed politeness, speaking in his best Eddie Haskell voice, rubbing the back of his neck where the whiplash had grabbed him.

"Anytime Kolo," I cooed.

"It's Kole," he spoke with resignation.

"Of course, Kole." I over-pronounced his name. "And I do hope your neck feels better soon."

I felt a twinge of remorse as I watched him limp unsteadily up the front walk and enter his house. He wasn't a bad boy, and I meant him no harm. In time, all three of us would master this delicate dating dance, deciding which partners deserved to glide along beside us, determining when to lead and when to follow. Next time I would barely tap the brakes until we found the right tempo to take us home.

I reached over to my daughter and patted her gently on the knee. "You never forget your first dance," I whispered to the breathtaking princess in the back seat.

"As if I ever could." She looked out the window and muttered more I didn't catch under her breath.

A soft smile formed on my lips as I pulled out carefully into the street. We took the long way home; there was no rush. We didn't hit a single animal along the way.

Splits Happen

Friday night arrives. Moms huddle in the bleachers wearing matching team shirts of royal blue, cameras posed. I search the field for my youngest daughter, Kristina, and sigh when I spot her sitting alone in the stands, looking down at her dance shoes. Once again, she won't be performing at half time.

I shake my head and mutter under my breath, "What a bunch of bull…"

"Splits!" The booster president focuses her camera. "I love this part!"

The award-winning Pacesetters high kick in sync, then leap and land in a line of perfect splits.

Splits happen, but not for my daughter. After years of reminding her to sit like a lady and keep her legs together, I encourage her to do the opposite.

"It's all in your head," I lie, knowing if there were a hundred-dollar bill on the ground, my calcified hamstrings would ignore it.

One game remains. Her last chance. I suggest hot baths and stretches. She rolls her eyes. Pilates and yoga. She scrolls down her phone. I promise fresh baked chocolate chip cookies if she'll practice, a bribe that never failed when she was younger. But now she's older with a smartphone and a mom she thinks is anything but.

"I can't! I'll tear a ligament!" She storms off into the kitchen. "And I'll make my own cookies!" She picks up a can of PAM and sprays a cloud of cooking oil all over the pan and most of the floor.

"Give me your phone!" I grab it and place it high on a shelf.

"Give it back!" she roars, a demon in a pair of black practice hot shorts.

"Practice your splits and you get the phone back."

Fury flashes across her face. Planting her hands on her hips, she slides one foot forward, lowering her body until it stops abruptly twelve inches from the floor. A split personality possesses her and she cries.

I soften. After all, the only thing I stretch these days is the truth. "That's better!" I cheer. "You're almost there."

The shrill ring of her phone breaks her concentration and she jumps up. We skid across the PAM coated kitchen tile, leap for the phone and with a horrible tearing sound and a scream, land in a tangled mess on the floor.

"Mom, look!" She waves her cell phone in the air like a pom-pom. "I'm doing the splits!" She rubs her legs in disbelief. "But I heard something tear."

"That was my pants." I clutch my lower back.

Friday night arrives and I lie in bed, a heating pad against my back. My daughter stops by wearing her blue and white game uniform and a smile. "I'm sorry you won't be able to see me dance." She hands me a plate of cookies. "The doctor said if you do your stretches, your back will get better." She pauses. "The pain's all in your head."

I roll my eyes, wave her away reaching for Advil. My back is killing me. Suddenly, I have a splitting headache.

Birds of a Feather

As a naïve young mother, I foolishly believed the pain of childbirth ended at delivery. I breathed a sigh of relief when the doctor I'd cursed under my breath for the last twelve hours handed me a perfect newborn baby girl and fled from the room, leaving me spread-eagle on the birthing table, a heap of heaving hormones. I shooed away my sleep-deprived husband and an over eager lactation specialist and smiled triumphantly at my daughter. *Baby girl, have I got plans for you!*

High on emotion and a well-placed epidural, I stared deeply into her innocent lapis blue eyes and promised her the moon, the stars, and all the silver jewelry I had hidden in a shoebox in my closet. I would be her protector, her soft place to land, the wind beneath her wings.

I'd been nesting for weeks in anticipation of welcoming the newest member of our family and couldn't wait to take her home, lay her down to sleep in her Winnie-the-Pooh crib and dress her in tiny outfits from the Gap. I was convinced the hard part was over now that she was finally here and healthy and ready to be held in my loving arms.

Little did I know, the hard part had just begun.

Flash forward twelve years.

I sat alone in my silver Mom-mobile, parked in line outside the school, nervously eating a bag of crushed Goldfish crackers I found in the console under a tangle of phone chargers that no longer charged and a melted Lancome lipstick in an unflattering shade. A bunch of blue and white congratulatory mums wrapped in pink cellophane waited expectantly in the empty passenger seat beside me. Impatient, I turned up the stereo. *I Gotta Feeling* by the Black-Eyed Peas blasted from the speakers. I threw back my head and smiled at the heavens. Surely this was a good sign!

Kristina had been practicing her cheer try-out routine to this song for weeks with three other girls from her class. The girls were inseparable in the days leading up to the try-outs and I rolled my eyes at the memory of Madeline, the shortest, loudest girl who snorted when she laughed, stopping and starting the song over and over again, demanding that my dance-challenged daughter point her toes and clap in time until the routine was perfect and each girl was assured a coveted spot on the cheer team. As a result, the whole family knew every word to the song and hummed the tune in their sleep.

The door to the school burst open and the first hopeful emerged, a petite blonde with a ponytail and a huge pair of pom-poms. I watched her race up to the first car in line and shriek through the open window to her equally blonde mother.

"I made it! I made it!" She laughed and cried and shook her pom-poms in the air, scaring away a flock of birds that had nestled in a tree nearby.

I shifted uncomfortably in my seat. *One down, five to go.*

A second girl skipped out of the school. I recognized her as the daughter of the perky PTA president. "Guess what? Guess what, guess what, guess what?" She danced a little jig and her mother flew out of the car and into her arms.

I hung my head and shook it slowly. *Guess that leaves four more.*

A split second later a third girl flew out of the building cart-wheeling into the convertible parked in front of me.

My mouth dropped open. *Three spots left.* I crossed my fingers and whispered a little prayer. She'd worked so hard for this. She *needed* this. I thought of all the lost spelling bees, the struggles in school, the drama with friends. Nothing seemed to come easily for Kristina. Now was her time to shine.

The Black-Eyed Peas sang happily in the background. I hoped it would be a very good night like they assured me it would be. I held my breath and waited.

The door swung open again and Kristina's three practice buddies danced out, arms linked together, talking excitedly. They spotted my car and sobered, smiled softly in my direction and ran on to share the good news with their mothers. They didn't notice a group of girls who filed out behind them, somber as a funeral procession, disappearing quietly one-by-one into waiting cars. A lump of dread formed in my stomach. Now I had a feeling that tonight was not gonna be a good night at all. I twisted the radio dial off and brooded in silence.

Minutes later the door to the school cracked open and Kristina slunk out, shoulders slumped, face blotched with tears. A wilted pom-pom peeked out of the top of her backpack. She held a neon flyer in her hand. My heart skipped a beat as I saw her stop to hug a girl waiting alone on a bench, crying. Then she slowly turned and started walking to the car. I threw the bouquet of flowers into the backseat, wiped my eyes with the back of my sleeve and put on my Positive Mom Mask.

She opened the car door and hurled her backpack into the back seat. I winced as I heard the cellophane wrapped around the flowers I'd bought her crinkle under the weight. I leaned towards her to give her a hug.

"I don't want to talk." She stared stoically ahead. "Just take me home." She looked down at the flyer in her hand, grunted, and wadded it into a ball.

But not before I read what it said. Mascot Try Outs. Two weeks away. Despite of, or because of, the pain in my heart, I began to devise a plan.

I discovered there's no greater fury than a cheer mother scorned. By the next afternoon, I'd tracked down the well-connected but intimidating mom of the current mascot to seek her help. Her daughter had tried out for cheerleader last year, lost, and earned her claim to fame shaking her tail feathers on the field as the proud Edgar the Eagle mascot. Since the girl would be flying off to high school next year, her mom agreed to take me under her wing and share some insider's secrets.

The mom arranged to meet with me where there was no chance of us being spotted, at a remote Starbucks two neighborhoods away. Wearing dark sunglasses and designer scarves draped over our heads, we met in a shadowy corner and bonded over our painful losses as we sipped over-priced lattes. Her wisdom didn't come cheap. I reached into my Kate Spade bag, drew out a slim envelope and slid it across the table. She nodded and slipped my generous donation towards the 8th grade dance into her Tory Burch.

"Bubbles," she whispered. "Lots of bubbles."

I raised my eyebrows.

"Bubbles and music, confetti poppers, glow sticks and candy. Lots of candy."

My mouth hung open. Was my daughter trying out or bribing the entire school to vote for her?

"The school frowns on fireworks." She took a long sip of her steamy drink and rolled her eyes in disgust. "Something about it being a safety issue."

I noticed with shock that she'd used an alias on her Starbucks cup.

"Look, your daughter's already lost out on being a cheerleader." She shook her head. "I wish you'd come talk to me sooner. I could've hooked you up with a cheer coach from the university." She removed her glasses and looked me straight in the eyes. "You gotta take no prisoners at the mascot try out." She crushed her paper cup; drops of milky coffee dripped down her manicured fingers. "And spare no cost to win."

I couldn't wait to share the news with Kristina when I picked her up from school.

"I don't want to be a stupid mascot." Kristina scowled at me, her braces flashing in the sun. "There's literally no way you're going to make me put on a sweaty old eagle costume and jump around in front of the whole school." She hurled her backpack into the backseat, crushing the props I'd just purchased at Party City for the try out. "If you think it's such a great idea, why don't *you* do it?" She stared out the window, red faced.

"Everyone loves the mascot!" I enthused. "You can be as crazy as you want and no one will remember it's you." I smiled to myself. In college it had been my secret dream to be the horned frog mascot at the TCU football games. I paused and reached across the seat to brush the hair out of her eyes. "And you'll be out on the field with your cheer friends. With Madeline and the other girls. You'd like that, wouldn't you?"

She seemed to consider this. "I guess. There's only one other person that I know of trying out—a boy named Buddy."

My heart leaped with hope. Only one contender! I reached into a bag from the back and pulled out a handful of candy, handing her a tootsie roll. As she chewed on the sweet nugget and contemplated my proposal, I turned on the stereo and pushed play. *Fly Like An Eagle* by the Steve Miller Band boomed from the speakers. Kristina rolled her eyes. I flapped my arms gracefully up and down to the beat, tickling my daughter's cheek with my fingertip. "Picture it."

She socked me in the wing. Then she picked up her cell phone and tapped out a number. "Hey Madeline," she said into the phone. "Guess what? I'm trying out for mascot."

We didn't waste any time perfecting her routine. Kristina had three minutes to wow the judges and the school and I was determined to make every moment count.

The morning of try outs we showed up at the school prepared for battle. Her nemesis, Buddy, a chubby boy with rosy cheeks and seasonal allergies, was already behind stage, looking more ostrich than eagle. When the announcer called for contestant number one, he walked nervously out onto the stage, tripping on his jumbo bird feet. Clearly, he was hoping to wing it.

Even wearing the full mascot costume, it was unlikely anyone would be fooled into believing he could jump more than a few inches from the floor, much less fly like an eagle to the sea. To make matters worse, in his hand he clutched a single, wrinkled, hand-made poster his mother clearly had not helped him make. "Vote Buddy for

Eagel!" it misspelled in large, blue block letters. He faced the crowd, shook like a dove during hunting season, and pointed at his poster. Then he lumbered off the stage to a weak round of applause.

The announcer introduced contestant number two next. I held my breath. For two weeks my daughter had done nothing but practice flying through the house, flapping her arms and pecking her head and finally she would have her chance to shine. She ran out onto the stage as a festive playlist of songs we created just for the try out boomed from the speakers. She blew bubbles, tossed confetti in the air, and performed a choreographed dance routine that culminated with Kristina shaking a pair of maracas and leading the entire front row of the auditorium in a massive congo line. The routine reached a jaw-dropping climax when my daughter miraculously soared into the air with the aid of ropes, pulleys and a buff custodian named Carlos, and showered the audience with tiny blue footballs emblazoned with *Vote for Kristina!* in gold glitter.

There was no way we could lose. Still, I didn't want to count my chickens before they hatched. That afternoon I waited in the carpool line, fingers crossed. When Kristina slumped out of the school, her hoodie covering most of her face, my heart dropped. I looked at her expectantly as she opened the door, heaved her backpack into the car and climbed in, avoiding my eyes.

"It was a close race." She leaned back on the headrest and shut her eyes.

"Close?" I'd seen the competition. There was no question who was the best eagle, who worked harder to win the coveted spot as mascot. I made mental plans to call the school the next day and demand a recount.

"But I made it."

I breathed a huge sigh of relief. "That's wonderful! It's going to be so much fun. Just you wait and ..."

She cut me off. "I hope you're happy. I literally do not want to spend my entire eighth grade year as an eagle."

* * *

The excited new cheerleaders and one unenthusiastic eagle were scheduled to perform at the next football game. I spent an hour helping Kristina into the colossal costume, packed her a cooler of water bottles to keep her refreshed under the hot Texas sun finishing with a pep talk as we drove to the football stadium. "I'm so excited for you," I began, trying to get used to seeing my daughter's frame transformed into a human-size bird body. "And I'm really proud of how you set a goal for yourself and worked hard to achieve it."

Kristina frowned at me, holding the eagle head on her lap. "I'm already hot." She pulled at the neckline of her costume. "And these feathers itch!"

"You just need to get used to being an eagle. It'll be fine." I parked the car and turned off the ignition. "Just remember to never take off your mask. You'll frighten the children."

I helped her out of the car, handed her a basket of candy to throw to her fans, and placed the eagle mask on her head.

"I can't see!" Her cry was muffled through the feathers.

I took her by the arm and led her to the entrance of the field. "Just a few more steps. Watch the curb."

"Do you not care that I can't see?" She started scratching her arms furiously, Sweet Tarts and Goobers flying out of her basket. "And I itch! This old bird is probably infested with lice, or fleas, or something." She bent down and scratched her yellow bird legs. "I hope I don't have chicken pox!"

Ignoring all protests, I guided my daughter to the edge of the Astroturf and gave her a gentle push onto the field.

"I'm hot. I'm going to faint. I can't see." She clung to me and then screamed, "My skin is on fire!"

The scoreboard was counting the seconds until halftime—in less than one minute (football time, so anywhere from one minute to thirty) Kristina would make her grand debut. I paused to relish the moment. Then I looked down at her arms.

Hives.

I twirled her around and marched her to the restroom. We burst into the handicap stall and I wrestled the heavy mask off her head. Her hair was matted against her face and drops of sweat poured down her cheeks. Kristina glared at me and plopped her tail on the toilet, refusing to budge.

"You can't just quit!" I looked down at her, hands on my hips. "They're about to call Edgar out onto the field." I stomped my foot. "The show must go on!"

In a fit of anger, she sprang up from the toilet and unzipped her costume, freeing herself from the nest of feathers. She kicked off her clawed shoes and peeled the yellow tights off her legs. I watched in horror as she, with a crazed gleam in her eye, dropped the sweaty mask onto my head. "Then *you* do it!"

Ten seconds later, I found myself jogging onto the field as the band played our fight song. I stared at the hundreds of spectators in blue and gave them a feeble wave. Then I froze. Somebody booed from the crowd. Refusing to be bullied, I remembered Super Frog from my college days and mustered some mom mojo. I flapped my arms in the air like I just didn't care, shook my hips to the beat of the music and hurled Dum Dum lollipops at the crowd, aiming at their feet so I didn't put out anyone's eyes. I high fived a cheerleader and ran a circle around a coach. Free as a bird, I shimmied and shook, hustled and grapevined. For my grand finale, I wound up my wings and propelled my body upward into a spread-eagle jump, soaring centimeters into the air and landing in a feathery middle-aged mound on the ground. I limped off the field before the medics arrived to carry me off on a stretcher.

That's when I spotted Buddy, sitting alone on a bleacher, shoulders slumped, head hung low. At the sight of his dejected face, my protective mom instincts went into high gear. I danced up to him in full eagle regalia, waving my arms in front of his face. When that didn't work, I reached into my candy basket and showered him with Twizzlers and Milk Duds. When the candy landed at his feet, ignored, I marched up to him and hissed, "Hey, kid. Meet me under the bleachers."

Minutes later we stood nose to beak in the dank shade, a stadium full of butts hanging comfortably over our heads.

"What do you want, Kristina?" Buddy whined.

I committed mascot cardinal sin number one and took off my mask. "Quick, put this on!"

Buddy recoiled in terror when he saw my sweaty, manic mom face in place of Kristina's pretty young one. He gasped and covered his eyes when he saw me struggle with the zipper of my costume and wiggle out of the suit.

"Don't chicken out now! Half-time's almost over." I helped him into the eagle disguise, smoothed his feathers and thrust the candy basket at him. "Buddy," I looked into his beady, sharp eagle eyes, "it's your turn to fly."

My heart full, I watched from under the bleachers as Buddy whooped and hollered and ran out onto the field. The butts overhead shifted in anticipation. To my amazement, Buddy paused at the fifty-yard line and transformed from a timid little wren into a powerful, regal eagle before my eyes. Then he exploded into a series of flips and twists and leaps across the field, finishing with a perfectly executed triple somersault. He landed in a graceful Russian split on the soft, green Astroturf, his downy feathers gently blowing in the autumn breeze. The crowd went wild.

No longer browbeaten Buddy, Edgar the Eagle jumped up and strutted off the field, proud as a peacock, a pretty cheerleader tucked under each wing.

I found Kristina at the concession stand holding a cherry snow cone. She was surrounded by her three cheer buddies who took turns patting her back and putting their arms around her shoulders as she gave an animated account of why her new job as Edgar the Eagle never got off the ground.

"It was so hot in that costume I almost fainted." Kristina fanned her face and bit into the icy treat. "I couldn't see out of the mask. I was literally blind."

Madeline dabbed at Kristina's brow with a wet napkin and invited all the girls to a sleepover after the game. My daughter's eyes lit up and her face broke into the first genuine smile I'd seen in weeks.

She was happy, so I was too.

I was paying for my diet Coke when a purple flyer on the bulletin board by the stand caught my eye. *Drama Club Try Outs! Next Week!* I snatched the notice off the wall and stuffed it in my purse. Kristina hugged her friends and linked arms with me. She smiled as she described in detail what she needed to pack for her sleepover with the girls as we walked to the car.

I took a long sip from my soda bottle and brushed my fingertips along the edge of the purple paper in my purse. I could see it now; her first starring role, my little drama queen's name in lights.

Baby girl, have I got plans for you.

Footnotes

My sixteen-year-old daughter, Kristina, is saving her toes for marriage. She announced this to me the day before she was to leave for Greece to attend a youth group camp at the Ionian Village. She had begged me for years to let her go on this priceless adventure to explore her heritage and discover herself. She insisted she was independent, mature, and responsible enough to leave the country without me.

This did not mean, however, that she was ready to pack for herself. She sat on her bed wearing mismatched socks and a scowl while I barked out the list of required items, checked her suitcase, and frantically scavenged through drawers and the bottom of her closet.

"Long skirts for visits to the monastery. Check," I began. "Modest one-piece swimsuit for free time at the pool. Check." I pretended I didn't see those rolled eyes. "Sandals for the beach and shower..." I paused, rummaging through ballet flats, pumps and a pair of combat boots; then looked at her expectantly.

"No way," she announced, her eyes daring me to challenge her.

"It's required." I pointed to the list. "You'll be in Greece. It's summer."

It was bad enough I was sending my youngest daughter across the world for three weeks to a camp where cell phones weren't allowed. I was sure her ADD would flare up and she would forget her Euros, her passport and how much she loved me. I had seen *Taken* too many times. My greatest fear was that she would be kidnapped, sold into the white slave trade, and never seen again.

My daughter's greatest fear, on the other hand, was wearing sandals.

When she was in first grade, I bought her a pair of pretty pink sandals with posies on the top. She put them on immediately, pirouetted through the house, and refused to take them off, even at bedtime. The next morning, she skipped onto the school bus proud to show off her new sandals to her classmates. That afternoon, she slumped off the bus wearing socks she'd borrowed from the nurse. It seems a fourth grader with a future foot fetish pointed out a fatal flaw. He noticed that instead of toes that descended from tallest to shortest like the Von Trapp family, my daughter's second toe stood out defiantly like an exclamation point.

"I'm a freak of nature!" she cried. She flung the offensive sandals high into the air before storming into the house. I watched them plop into a puddle, float for a second, then slowly sink into the mud.

When she grew older, she researched reconstructive toe surgery that would beautify the line of her toes, giving her perfect little piggies. She considered binding her second toe to stunt its growth until the others could catch up. She threatened to chop off a half inch from each offending digit with a pair of yard clippers. Finally, she vowed to never again show her toes in public to spare herself future humiliation. Only her husband, if any man would even want to marry her with this deformity, would ever lay eyes on her naked toes.

"You're being ridiculous!" I argued with her that night, stomping my own familial foot for emphasis. "Be thankful you have ten toes, at all! Stand up for yourself and be proud of who you are. I have the same toes as you. I managed to survive."

"You don't understand! You never understand. You're old." Her voice caught. "No one cares if *you're* deformed." She sobbed and I hung my head, defeated, agonizing how my smart, beautiful daughter could be so shallow.

I looked down at my own feet, freshly pedicured in hot pink polish, wearing bejeweled sandals that shouted for attention. But it had not always been this way. I flashed back to my own youth and then long forgotten feelings of inadequacy crept back. I remembered a young, insecure version of myself standing barefoot by a pool, curling my toes under my feet so no one would see them. When I was her age, my mother's well-meaning words did little to comfort me either.

"We're going shopping," I announced to my teenager. My mother taught me long ago that shopping cures everything. I was determined the perfect pair of sandals would save my daughter's sole.

I cajoled and pleaded with her in the car on the way to the mall. She finally agreed to look at the sandals, possibly purchase a pair, but she would not try them on in the store, and would not guarantee she would ever wear them on her trip. When we walked into Sun and Ski she pretended an interest in Yeti containers while I browsed the sandal selection.

A young man approached and asked if I needed any help. I looked up at him, catching my breath. He had curly brown hair, a twinkle in his eye, and the intoxicating smell of new shoes. He was built like a Greek god in a pair of Nikes.

"My daughter needs some thongs," I stammered. "For Greece." I saw her dive under a rack of hoodies from the corner of my eye. "For her...feet."

He smiled and I melted. "Where is your daughter?" I pointed to her sneakered feet peeping out from beneath the rack. I watched incredulously as he parted the clothes, reached for her hand and led her to a chair. He removed my daughter's shoes and measured her feet. "Wait here while I find you some sandals," he said and disappeared before she could protest. She gave me a murderous look and flipped me off with one of her middle toes. "I can't believe you're making me do this," she hissed. "I don't even want to go to Greece, anymore!"

"I can't believe how ungrateful you are!" I hissed back. "Anyone would jump at the chance to go on a trip like this!"

She could deal with prince charming all by herself. Already he had returned, balancing a mountain of shoe boxes in his muscular arms. He kneeled at her feet and gingerly reached for the cuff of her sock. I cringed. She glanced at me, mortified, her eyes begging me to come to her aid, but I stepped away, knowing I couldn't help with this one. I began to think of me to keep my mind off her anguish: How I would appreciate another opportunity to go to Greece. I had not been since I was her age, when my father was finally able to take off work so we could go on a family trip to the village where he had been born...

I remember my parents making us visit one boring museum after another when all my sister and I wanted to do was to lie out on a beach, flirt with Greek boys and swim in the cobalt sea. We must have looked at a thousand Greek statues when I made a life-altering discovery. Each statue, *every* statue, had second toes that stood out defiantly from the rest. A placard on the wall informed us that this anomaly was a sign of aristocracy and beauty to the ancient Greeks. Elated, we took photos of the statues and compared their strong, grounded feet with ours. We snapped shots of me barefoot behind the statues, and laughed that I was following in the footsteps of our great ancestors.

We finally had the chance to lay out by the pool at the hotel our last day in Athens. For once in my life, I stretched out unselfconsciously on the chaise lounge. For the first time, I did not try to hide my toes under the rubber slat of the chair or cover my feet with a beach towel. I was a cosmopolitan woman of the world, feeling the pleasant sensation of the Mediterranean sun on my bikini-clad body. I closed my eyes, finally at peace with myself and the toes God had given me. My sister with her normal toes was almost jealous of my authentic Greek ones.

I was drifting off to sleep when suddenly I felt a pinch on my right second toe, like a bird had swooped down to bite it, mistaking it for a worm. Startled, I opened my eyes to find a man at my feet, sporting a hairy chest, a Speedo and a leer.

"I love your toes!" he exclaimed in perfect English. "Beautiful girl, beautiful toes!" I blushed from head to toe under my Grecian tan as he walked away.

I sat up and looked at my sister in the next chair. My greatest nightmare had come true. A strange man had not only spotted my offensive digit, but had the audacity to violate it with his hand. Had he grabbed a huge hunk of my bikini bottom I would not have been more mortified. My sister and I stared at each other in horror, mouths gaping open, sharing a silent scream like only teenage girls can do. Then we howled with laughter.

I should have kicked him in the face. I should have lectured him on boundaries and proper pool etiquette and reported him to the authorities. Instead, I fantasized marrying this man who had worshipped my toes, bringing him back to America where I would live happily ever after enjoying foot massages and open-toed shoes.

My daughter interrupted these thoughts. "Mom, which ones do you like?" She smiled broadly as she examined her feet. Wearing a Teva on her right foot and a Sanuk on her left, she paraded up and down the aisle for me as the salesman looked on, nodding his head in approval. He stopped her and got down on one knee to adjust a strap, his fingers lightly grazing a long toe, a look of appreciation on his chiseled face. She gazed down at him, clearly head over heels.

I pulled out my credit card and handed it to the boy. "We'll take them both," I said, winking at my daughter.

She wore the Tevas out of the store, no longer afraid to put her best foot forward, and we hurried home to finish packing. Today she bought new sandals. Tomorrow she would travel to Greece and explore a new world. Next year she would start college; rushing down the road to self-discovery. Perhaps she would find something more valuable to save for her husband.

For now, I was happy to foot the bill.

Excess Baggage

Growing up, some of the happiest (and most harrowing) memories I have are of taking our family version of a vacation. My mother would spend months planning for the adventure, collecting maps and brochures, booking tours, and making reservations. My brother and sister and I would wait all year for the magical moment in the middle of summer when our dad would sacrifice two whole days off from work to chauffer the entire family to my mother's latest dream destination.

We would pile into our maroon Lincoln Continental, my brother sandwiched between my mom and dad in the front seat, holding a thermos of hot coffee between his legs, and my sister and I crammed into the back seat with Yaya and Poppy. We'd count windmills to pass the time as we drove, stopping every few miles so one of us could use the restroom at a seedy gas station, or, if carsick, vomit into a brown paper bag. Going on a trip, even to Galveston, which was only one hour away from our home on Hillcroft, was momentous. A weekend on Padre Island was earth-shattering. Once we even made it as far as the border, and vacationed in lovely Laredo, Texas, so my mom could shop for huge colorful clay pots and man-sized suits of armor which my dad artfully strapped to the roof of the car for the long drive home.

Through the mishaps and mayhem, all that mattered was that we were together. The destinations weren't exotic or exciting, but we explored them like a team of travel advisors, leaving no scenic overlook unseen, no rest stop unstopped. We were having fun, which the blurry, red-tinged photos of us with our eyes closed would prove later. And all that frantic family fun made returning home even sweeter.

I longed to give my children the gift of travel, too. As an overwhelmed single mother with three teenagers, I worried that my children wouldn't get the chance to experience the world outside of Katy, Texas. I feared they'd never know there were entire countries out there where kids didn't study at Starbucks over five-dollar lattes and go back-to-school shopping at Hollister. I fretted they'd never discover whole continents existed where moms didn't drive SUVs the size of living rooms and carpool entire soccer teams to practice. Most importantly, I wanted to give them a trip they'd never forget and a reason to remember me long after I'd flown off to my final destination.

So I morphed into my mother. But while she had to write to the chamber of commerce and wait weeks for them to mail her travel information, it took me mere seconds to search the internet for vacation discounts and promotions. Scraping up frequent flier miles and instilling the help of a helpful AAA travel agent, I managed to create the dream vacation of a lifetime. Soon Spain beckoned us like a flamenco dancer. Italy and France serenaded us from afar.

We'll see lavender fields, the Coliseum, Monaco! I encouraged the kids to research the historical places we'd visit, to Google La Sagrada Familia and the statue of David. I printed out articles for them to read. The more prepared we were, the more we'd enjoy ourselves.

"Make sure you pack some spare underwear in your carry-on," I warned them. I knew from traveling with my family as a young girl that many trips which started with high hopes for adventure ended with lost luggage, or worse.

"That's lame," they grumbled in unison and rolled their eyes. After all, any time an object couldn't be found, which meant it wasn't conveniently placed directly under one of their noses, all any of them had to do was yell, "Mom!" at the top of their lungs and I would race to the rescue, finding the misplaced but irreplaceable item in under three minutes. As a result, though they'd never admit to being lost without me, besides an occasional basketball game or baby tooth, they'd never really *lost* anything at all.

In the end, each child interpreted my nuggets of travel wisdom differently. My son, full of angst at being forced to travel with a family full of females, was only concerned about packing his game boy and two weeks' worth of new cartridges into the backpack he would bring on the plane. My youngest daughter, worried about starving to death in countries that might not specialize in chicken nuggets, stuffed enough Pop-Tarts, goldfish and Teddy Grahams in her carry-on to serve the entire economy class round-trip. Only my older daughter took my advice seriously and purchased an entire summer wardrobe from Forever 21 just for the trip, and smartly tucked an extra pair of underwear and a swimsuit into a stylish tote. She wanted to look perfect for pictures.

The week before our trip, I bought us matching blue suitcases and tied each handle with a large red bow so we'd be able to spot ours amongst all the boring black bags at the airport. The night before leaving I supervised each child as they packed, making sure no necessities were left behind, examining the outfits they planned on wearing on the plane and triple-checking that each piece of luggage was clearly labeled.

When I caught them snickering behind my back, I shared a family vacation horror story with them to defend my actions. When I was in high school, my parents were finally able to take me and my younger sister and brother on a European vacation. Miraculously, my dad left his business for three glorious weeks and we were ecstatic about taking our first trip overseas. I dressed in my favorite peppermint striped sundress, which was the perfect summer outfit for a sixteen-year-old in Houston, but a poor choice for June abroad. When we landed in Madrid and wandered through a crowd of locals wearing sweaters and jeans, I stuck out like a sore candy cane. Worse yet, when each member of my family grabbed a suitcase from the carousel at the airport, mine was nowhere to be found.

My kids groaned. That was back in the Stone Age. That would never happen now, they argued. Suitcases didn't even have wheels back then!

That night I pleaded with my little sister, who was two sizes smaller than I was and going through a punk rock stage, to let me borrow something, anything, to wear. She dug through the piles of clothing in her suitcase and forced herself to loan me an Ozzy Osbourne t-shirt. And, since my hot rollers were making waves somewhere without me, she generously offered to help me style my hair, naturally.

"I read how to do this in Teen magazine." She brushed her dark, glossy straight hair in front of the mirror while she waited for me to me wash my thick, unruly mane with the cheap shampoo provided by the hotel. "I'll make a bunch of tiny braids all over your head, then tomorrow when we take them out, you'll have soft waves around your face. You'll love it!"

When I protested there was no conditioner, much less styling mousse, to tame my frizzy locks, she rolled her eyes. Almost in tears, I sat on the bed wearing her faded black concert t-shirt over my day-old underwear and allowed her to pull and twist my wet hair into tiny plaits.

The kids looked at me with interest. "Auntie Annie's so cool," my youngest daughter said.

I rolled my eyes and went on with my story. The next morning, I redressed in my wrinkled red and white striped outfit while she tried on an assortment of studded jeans and shredded shirts she dug out of her un-lost luggage. After she was dressed in the height of punk fashion, down to a spiked dog collar around her neck, she sat me on the bed and began unbraiding the snakelike ropes. They seemed to have multiplied on my head overnight, transforming me into a modern-day Medusa.

"I can't loosen some of these." Ignoring my screams, she yanked on a stubborn braid, ripping a fistful of hair out of my scalp. After twenty more minutes of agonizing labor, she stood back, hands on her black leather belt to admire her handiwork. "It's not bad." She reached up to smooth a kinky patch over my ear. "Definitely makes a statement."

I got off the bed, ran to the bathroom mirror and shrieked at the image staring back at me. My naturally wavy hair frizzed into a foot-high hedge around my face. "I look like an electrocuted clown!" I tore at the halo of hair on my head. "I'm a fuzz covered Christmas candy from the bottom of Yaya's purse." My eyes filled with frustrated tears. "I can't be seen like this!"

"I don't know why you're mad at *me!*" my sister yelled back. "I was only trying to help."

My kids stared at me, shaking their heads. "Mom, you're so dramatic!"

I raised my eyebrows. "Until you've walked a mile in my sister's one-size-too small jellies, don't judge me."

My naïve children persisted. "Couldn't your parents have helped you?" It was impossible for them to imagine going without full on family assistance.

I recalled the economy size bottle of Aqua Net my mother kept on her bathroom sink next to my dad's small jar of Brylcreem. "No." I shook my head sadly. "No one could help me."

We returned to packing—which for my children, involved frantically stuffing the entire contents of their dresser drawers into their suitcases. Only my older daughter gave any real thought to what she would be wearing. She paused and spun around in a circle, modeling a new strapless dress she'd chosen to wear on the plane, admiring the flounce of the skirt. "What do you think Mom?"

I eyed the sheer fabric and opened my mouth to protest, but smiled softly as I watched her pose in front of the mirror. Then she rejoined the others. They bounced on their suitcases, smashing the contents inside and tugging the zippers closed.

On the way to the airport the next day, I conducted a crash course in foreign phrases. "It's important that we respect the culture of the countries we're visiting." I yanked the headphones off of the nearest child's ears. "And we need to learn a few words so we can communicate." I pursed my lips and annunciated in my best Pepé Le Pew accent, "*Oui, non, pardon.*" By the time we checked in our over-stuffed bags and boarded our plane at the Air France terminal, though we were far from fluent, with exaggerated facial expressions and wild gestures, I figured we'd get by. By the time we watched a couple of complementary in-flight movies, attempted to nap in the cramped seats, and snacked on microwaved croissants, we'd landed in Spain just in time to catch our cruise to France.

"*Pardon?*" I reached for the flight attendant's sleeve as she sauntered past. Although the plane had landed almost half an hour earlier, Air France had no ants in its pants to deplane its passengers.

She slowed and scowled at me. "*Oui?*"

My children perked up as they caught the exchange. Their mother was actually conversing in French and so far they could understand every word.

I pointed to my watch, which was still set to Houston time and frowned. "We have a cruise to catch." I spoke loudly and slowly, nodding my head to emphasize each word. "Big boat. One hour."

The flight attendant rolled her eyes and answered me in a strong Brooklyn accent, "Well, maybe you should have given yourself more time to get off the big plane." She shrugged, unconcerned, and wandered away, leaving a trail of French perfume behind her.

I wrung my hands and clutched the strap of my purse. We still had to collect our luggage, go through customs, and catch a shuttle to the port. A few minutes later a male voice crackled over the speaker. I caught every other word: "Sorry...Delay...Soon."

"Hey Mom, did you hear that?" My son poked me in the arm. "It doesn't sound like—" he paused and exaggerated the next word, *"oui* are going to catch our cruise."

As soon as the plane doors opened, I formed a conga-line with my kids and hustled them off the aircraft and into the terminal, leaving a trail of Goldfish behind.

"I have to pee!" My youngest daughter stopped suddenly when she saw the restroom sign and crossed her legs.

Her brother eyed the food court.

"You can pee on the boat!" I yanked at her arm and glared at my son. "And eat there, too. No one stops until we're on that ship." I glanced at my watch and struggled to calculate how late we were in French time. "Our ship is sailing soon. And I'm going to be on it with a frozen drink in my hand, with or without you!"

In the next harrowing hour, I learned that although in the states I was a multi-tasking supermom who could fly over obstacles without chipping my manicure, here I was a mere mortal whose American charm didn't translate, and no one could understand my cries for help.

"What do you mean our luggage isn't here?" I wrung my hands together and pleaded with an unconcerned Air France airport employee sporting a French goatee who murmured a half-hearted apology and signaled to the next in line. My eyes darted hopefully to the baggage carousel which had sputtered to a stop fifteen minutes before, but our matching blue bags were nowhere in sight. "We're going on a cruise! There's no time to wait for them to come on the next flight." I pounded on the counter. "We're on our way to catch the shuttle to the dock right now."

The employee glanced up at a lazy clock on the wall. "Madame, you have already missed the last shuttle to the port. Perhaps you can get a hotel room and we will deliver your luggage to you tonight." He shrugged. "Or in the morning. Then tomorrow you can catch a flight to your first port of call."

I wanted to leap over the counter and grab the little man by his scrawny, pale neck. "I'm NOT missing that boat!"

He glanced down at my Nike cross trainers with disdain and raised his eyebrows. "Then I suggest you run."

We tore off to the nearest taxi stand and leaped into the first cab. "To the port!" I cried to the startled driver who threw his half-smoked cigarette out the window. "And make it fast!"

I checked to make sure the kids had their seatbelts on, then held onto the dashboard for dear life as we took off, dodging in and out of traffic. By the time we spotted the *Majesty of the Sea*, passengers were lining up for the muster drill. Thousands of smiling passengers wearing bright orange life vests lined the decks of the ship, waving as it sounded its horns. More than a few of them pointed to us, amused by the three straggly teen-aged latecomers who ran by the deserted check-in booth and raced up the ramp as the final horn sounded, and the one middle-aged mother jogging to keep up.

I could barely breathe from the exertion. We limped up to the ship's information desk. The purser, wearing a crisp white uniform and a brass nametag with *Lars* engraved on it, took in our disheveled state. "I'm so glad you could join us. Running a bit late, are we?" He glanced at our rumpled clothes. "Need some help with your luggage?"

My youngest daughter, near tears, plopped her pink backpack onto his desk. A school of Goldfish swam towards him and he brushed them aside.

"Bringing food onto a cruise ship is a bit like bringing sand onto the beach," he observed with a twitch of a smile, clearly impressed with his own wit.

I threw my hands up in the air. "Our luggage is lost."

"We don't have anything to wear," wailed my oldest daughter.

"Not to worry." Lars dug around under his desk. "We have everything you need on board." He pulled out four Royal Caribbean t-shirts and plopped them on the desk. "These are complimentary, of course!"

The girls, grieving over the contents of their lost suitcases, were hysterical. My son, suffering from a combination of hunger, anger and too much estrogen invading his personal space, looked like he wanted to punch something. Hard. I looked down at the wrinkled shirt and jeans I was wearing and wanted to jump ship. *At least it's not a peppermint-striped sundress this time!*

I gathered us together for a pep talk. "Look, we're all in the same boat," I began. When that didn't get any smiles, I changed tactics. "Tomorrow when our luggage gets here, we'll all have a good laugh over this."

Lars perked up. "Oh, you won't get your luggage tomorrow." He shook his head. "Or the next day. We'll be at sea." He glanced at the ship itinerary and smiled broadly. "But I do have good news! The captain's dinner is tomorrow. You won't want to miss that. Everyone gets dressed up and..."

Lars obviously wasn't the sharpest anchor in the sea.

I pursed my lips together and scowled at him.

"Oh, right." He hung his head, rubbed a hand through his thick blonde waves, then looked up at us and smiled. "I have an idea." He pointed at my son. "What are you, a 40 long?" He scribbled something on a card and handed it to my son. "This is good for a free tuxedo rental."

Lars looked at my daughters and me. "And for you ladies, I have a special treat." He glanced around and lowered his voice, "We have a private closet full of beautiful gowns. If you promise not to tell anyone, I will take you there and let you choose a dress for the captain's dinner."

The girls' eyes lit up. Even I was smitten. *Beautiful gowns!* I'd seen pictures of what some of the performers wore in the nightly shows and blushed. I imagined a secret dressing room, tucked away behind stage, filled with racks of jewel toned, sequined costumes with thigh high slits and plunging necklines.

I shook my head at Lars. "Oh no, we couldn't!"

In my fantasy, I choose the perfect gown and slide it up my hips, aroused by the feel of the sparkling fabric embracing my body. That night, the captain, a stoic, blue-eyed Norwegian, sees me from across the room and catches his breath. Besotted with my beauty, he no longer requires a woman in every port. Instead of driving a Ford, I'm cruising the fjords, sipping champagne with my new commanding officer on our own private Loveboat.

Then I remembered my only pair of Spanx was lost somewhere between Houston and Barcelona and my face fell. Even a strategically placed boa and a huge feather headdress couldn't hide my penchant for midlife buffets.

"But I insist," Lars interrupted my fantasy. "Follow me." He led us down to a lower deck and guided us through a long corridor. Pausing outside an unassuming door, he tapped a code into the keypad.

"It's all yours." He bowed slightly and like a game show host, waved his arm with an exaggerated flourish. "Our secret Saks Fifth Avenue of the Sea." He flipped a lock of hair out of his eyes and lowered his voice. "Compliments of Royal Caribbean."

I looked up at Lars and smiled, thankful that for at least one evening we would feel so glamorous we would forget our bags were stuck in the land of lost luggage. I held my breath, anticipating the collection of gorgeous gowns the girls and I would get to sample. We slipped into the dimly lit closet-sized room. I blinked as my eyes adjusted to the low lighting, then gasped and covered my mouth.

My shoulders slumped as I spied a handful of tired dresses hanging hopelessly in a row. Where the jewel-toned beaded gowns of my imagination should have been displayed, cheap wire hangers sagged under the weight of polyester and perspiration. A musty scent of mothballs and discarded dreams greeted us, and I wrinkled my nose.

"Looks more like Sucks Fifth Avenue," my son muttered under his breath, twirling the free tux rental card in his hand.

"It's not so bad," I said bravely, pulling a faded floral prairie dress off the rack and holding it in front of my body. "Shoulder pads are slimming."

My younger daughter reached out to touch a wrinkled navy dress with a sailor collar. "The zipper's broken," she whispered.

My oldest daughter burst into tears. "I'd rather walk the plank."

Every dress we picked up was defective. Missing buttons, drooping hemlines, unexplainable stains, each fashion don't was sadder than the last. If my peppermint-striped sundress from decades past had been stuffed in a back corner, I wouldn't have been surprised. Clearly the Saks of the Sea was little more than a glorified lost and found of forgotten frocks.

Lars gazed at us, eyes glistening with emotion. "I can see you're overwhelmed. There are so many to choose from!" He backed out of the room. "I have to get back to work now, but please take all the time you need. I'm just so glad I could help."

We discussed our dilemma before bed that night, all four of us wearing matching Royal Caribbean shirts. We were tempted to ditch the captain's dinner the next day altogether, eat soft-serve ice-cream cones by the pool, and call it a night.

The next day we hung out near our cabin, feeling sorry for ourselves, but by the afternoon hunger and thoughts of the filet mignon and lobster we'd be missing led us to investigate the overpriced onboard gift shop. So when my son returned back to the cabin to change into his freshly pressed tuxedo, the girls and I raced to the tiny store that promised gold chains by the foot and pashminas for only ten dollars. We skidded into the door five minutes before closing.

"We've lost our luggage." I stared up at the shopkeeper, a tall, mustached man shaped like a French baguette with a *Pierre* nametag over his right breast pocket.

The corner of his mouth twitched and he glanced at his watch. He pointed to a wall with rhinestone studded bikinis and floppy straw hats.

"You don't understand. I'm sure we'll get our luggage back any minute now, but for the time being, we need real clothes." I glanced at the bikini display. "To actually wear in public."

"We have nothing!" my older daughter burst out, her face red.

He seemed to consider this for a moment, then gestured to another wall. Cheap rain ponchos, foreign sunscreen and Dramamine lined the shelves. My daughter started hyperventilating. Ignoring her meltdown, he began counting the change in the cash drawer.

I wanted to jump over the counter and strangle the smirk off his face. "We need real clothes. Dresses, pants." I pointed to my face. "Makeup!" Lowering my voice, I leaned closer to him saying, "We don't even have the bare necessities."

His pencil thin eyebrows shot up. "I see." Reaching into his pocket, he pulled out a ring of keys and strode to the back of the store. He scooted a selection of sarongs out of the way and leaned down to unlock a cabinet, hidden behind the merchandise.

I drew in my breath. *What was it with these crewmembers and their secret stashes?* I tried to imagine what sort of underwear was so delicate, so valuable, that it had to be in a safe under lock and key. I peered over his shoulder as he reached for the only item in the cabinet. I expected silk or satin, leather or lace. Instead, he thrust a three-pack of Hanes for Her XXXL plus size panties in shocking white at me, then wiped his hands on his pants as if they were sullied.

I pried the package open with my fingernail and pulled out a pair. I held up the portly panty in front of my hips and the no-roll elastic waistband rested under my nose. A granny wouldn't be caught dead in these panties. My whole family could fit in this pair of panties. I was fairly certain if the engine failed, the ship could cruise around the world with only this panty as a sail.

"I'll pass on the panties." I heard the girls exhale in unison. "But we'll take three of those sarongs."

My son looked like a young James Bond that night. His tailored tux fit his athletic body perfectly. If anyone noticed the three females he escorted into the formal dining room for the captain's dinner were wearing artfully tied swimsuit cover-ups hiding questionable underwear, no comment was made. We feasted on filet mignon and lobster, clapping as our waiter served a flaming Baked Alaska. For two glorious hours we forgot about what we didn't have; focusing instead on what we did.

I took another sip of wine and spotted the captain across the room, surrounded by beautifully dressed, important looking people. If he noticed the woman resembling a castaway, wearing a tropical beach cover-up and a yard's worth of gold chain around her neck, her hair in untamed waves, he probably wouldn't have invited her to sail the world with him, and she probably wouldn't have cared. She was having too much fun.

Tomorrow I'd worry about our luggage again. I'd grill the front desk and call the airline. But tonight, the ship rocked gently as it crossed the ocean, and we could see the brilliant twinkling of the stars through the dining room windows. I looked at my children, laughing with each other about our first two days of adventure, and realized everything we needed was at our little table. We had food, and wine, and senses of humor. Most of all, we had each other. Maybe the things we lost were things we didn't need after all— just excess baggage.

Tomorrow we would dock at our first port of call. It would be nice to tour Nice in proper clothes. But if we had to, we'd wear the same outfits seven days in a row.

And there's nothing sarong about that.

Northern Heights

I swore this would be the last time I'd go out on a limb for my kids...When they were younger and I would announce to them we were going on a family vacation, they would clap and cheer and run off to pack their little Disney suitcases full of their favorite toys. They didn't care where we were going as long as they could stay in a motel with a pool. I was their hero, a young, cool mom with a fold-out map and a picnic basket. They'd cheerfully follow me to the ends of the earth and write about their adventures on postcards they'd send to their envious friends.

But they were older now, and few things were worth writing home about.

I wanted to curse the day I came home from the AAA store armed with travel brochures and a huge smile. It was a gorgeous spring day in Houston; I had just booked a once-in-a-lifetime trip for my teenaged daughters, my parents, and me. I could barely contain myself. The only thing that would have made me happier was if my son could come with us, but his brand-new job in Dallas didn't allow him to traipse across the country like a carefree college student.

When I walked through the door, my twenty-year-old daughter, Kati, an aspiring photographer in her second year at Texas A&M, paused long enough to look up from her laptop where she was editing photos. She observed the blue AAA bag in my hand and eyed me suspiciously. "Please tell me you didn't book anything for July. I'm working every weekend in July."

Her seventeen-year-old sister, Kristina, a high school senior with a perpetual case of spring fever, sensed big news and muted the show she was watching on Netflix. "I hope it's Hawaii! Or Mexico! Any place with a beach and fruity drinks." She leaped up from the sofa and stretched. "I'm so pale! And I'll need a new swimsuit." She grabbed for the brochure in my hand. "So where are we going, Mom?"

My smile dimmed, but I was determined not to let them dampen my excitement. "I don't know. Do *Juneau*?" I exaggerated the last word, drawing out the first syllable.

"No," Kristina said, slowly pronouncing each word. "That's why I want to see the *bro-chure*."

Kati's lip curled. "Alaska, stupid. She's taking us to Alaska. I bet it's a cruise."

Her younger sister's face fell. "Alaska cruises are for old people." She slumped back down on the sofa, pulled out her cell phone and began to text, no doubt reporting the unfairness of her life to her best friend. "Boring." She looked up at me and rolled her eyes. "So much for getting a tan."

I tried to hide my disappointment and went into my bedroom to call my mother. She answered on the tenth ring, and I sprung my surprise, knowing at least I could count on her to be thrilled about my gift.

"Alaska?" My mother paused for so long, I thought she had hung up or fainted from excitement. "It's cold in Alaska. And it's for..." she hesitated and then whispered, "old people."

It was then I made the horrifying realization that I had just booked a trip to the only state in the United States that apparently catered to the ninety-something crowd. Worse yet, if I was the only one who thought it sounded fun, maybe I was the old one.

My apprehension only grew in the weeks leading up to the trip. My mother called me daily: to go over what she was packing, to fret over whether her fur coat would be warm enough, or to question where she could purchase long underwear for my dad in July. She packed and repacked gloves and scarves, boots and hats, certain she and my dad would freeze, even though I argued it would be summer in Alaska too.

My daughters, on the other hand, put off packing until the night before. Between the two of them, they brought three mittens and one long-lost hoodie they found in the bottom of the hall closet for warmth, but somehow the weight of their suitcases still managed to exceed the airline's limit.

As we waited in line at the cruise terminal in Seattle, I took on the impossible role of keeping my travel companions happy. The girls were satisfied as long as their cell phones were charged, Wi-Fi was available, and they were receiving an acceptable number of likes on Instagram. I was thrilled we all had our luggage.

My parents proved to be more challenging. My dad needed food, and lots of it. My mother required coffee to cope. Both struggled to keep up, barely visible behind the mountain of carry-ons they balanced in their arms. Still, even with their slower pace, neck pillows, and coolers full of medication, I couldn't help noticing they were two of the youngest people in line to embark on the ship.

I had the sinking feeling we were boarding the *Titanic* of vacations. "This is going to be so much fun!" My cheerful tone sounded fake even to me. I directed everyone to the excursion booth. "Let's book some activities before they're all sold out."

"I'm getting something to eat, then taking a nap." My dad shuffled off in search of the nearest buffet. Broad as a bull and just as strong, his posture read that he was on vacation and he was going to do whatever he wanted, with or without us. He whistled for my mom to follow.

I studied the list of excursions. This would be a fun, memorable vacation if it killed me. "How about a ride in a vintage railcar through the scenic mountains?"

"Boring!" the girls chimed in unison.

"No trains," my mom called over her shoulder to me as she rushed to catch up with my dad. "Trains are dangerous. Some shopping. Maybe a bus tour of the city."

I examined the ad for the train ride again. *Enjoy panoramic views of mountains, glaciers, gorges, and waterfalls,* it read. How much safer could you get? The most challenging part of this excursion would be getting their cabooses all aboard.

"We'll take two tickets for the train." It would do my parents good to get out of their comfort zone for a couple of hours. "Now for us . . ."

"Dog sledding!" Kristina pointed to a picture of a team of huskies pulling a sled through the snow. "The three-hour trip includes flightseeing via helicopter and one hour at a dog sled camp," she read. "And we get to see two glaciers. Now that would be fun!"

"You know I'm afraid of heights." My heart pounded at the thought of boarding a helicopter and almost stopped altogether when I saw the price. "Besides, that excursion costs more than the entire cruise! Let's look for something more reasonable we can all enjoy." I wiped the sweat off my brow with the back of my hand; my eyes begged the excursion director for help.

She pointed to a picture of a family wearing matching helmets and huge smiles. "May I suggest our Alaska Canopy Adventure?" She gave me a subtle once over and erased the beginnings of a smirk off her face. "It's very popular with our younger, more adventurous guests. Entirely safe, of course." She studied my face for a moment. "Unless you'd rather go on the train ride with your parents..."

"Alaska Canopy Adventure it is." *Whatever that is.* I pulled out my Visa card and thrust it at the young woman behind the counter. "You only live once!"

I linked arms with the girls as we headed down the long corridor to our cabin, pausing for me to kiss each one gently on the forehead. It took so little to make them happy. My heart soared at the joy I saw on their faces.

"I can't wait for tomorrow! I'm going to get the best photos, ever." Kati looked at me with admiration in her eyes. "I'm so proud of you, Mom. Facing your fears like that."

I froze. "What do you mean?"

"Zip-lining? Tomorrow? Nonrefundable?" She pointed to the tickets I clutched in my hand and read the fine print out loud. "Enjoy the thrill of gliding through the top of a rich rainforest canopy over eight zip lines and three suspension bridges one hundred thirty-five feet above the forest floor." She watched the blood drain from my face. "Mom, are you okay?"

Kristina fanned me with a map of Juneau, brown eyes wide with concern. "What's there to worry about?" She looked genuinely puzzled. "You'll be wearing a helmet."

The next morning I woke with a dreadful feeling in my stomach and the metallic taste of terror on my tongue.

Three things forced me out of my cozy cabin bed: the mental image of my mother, who I feared I was turning into if I didn't fly out of my comfort zone, and my two pushy daughters standing at the foot of my bed, hands on their hips. For once, they were up before me, already dressed for adventure.

Kristina wrestled me out of my bunk, a determined look on her face. "Rise and shine," she sang in her best morning-mom impression. She took in my watery eyes and slumped shoulders. "You literally look like you've just lost your phone, or worse. It's going to be fun."

Kati took over. "Seriously, Mom. I've done this before. You'll be fine." She handed me a cup of coffee and my running shoes. "And we'll get the greatest pictures." Poised and unflappable, she strapped her camera bag over her shoulders and looked me up and down with the critical eye of a photographer. "Is that what you're wearing?"

I took a sip of the scalding coffee, summoned my inner warrior, and eyed the two confident young women in front of me, leaders in Lycra leggings. I wasn't getting any younger, their expressions screamed at me. I'd better live a little while I still could.

I warmed up to the idea as we left the ship and met others who were going to be joining us on this excursion. Everyone was happy and excited, I almost forgot the fear that simmered deep in my bowels. I even enjoyed the Jeep ride through the Tongass National Forest. In my quest to spot a black bear with the other eager tourists, I didn't notice how high we were climbing up the winding roads.

Somehow, I allowed the tour guides—a perky blonde with pigtails and her partner, a hunky bearded lumberjack with a man bun— to slip a leather harness up my legs and around my waist.

In denial, I followed the others up a steep stairway wrapped around a massive trunk until all twelve of us circled the tree, over a hundred feet up, perched on a wooden platform no larger than my coffee table. I clutched the trunk for dear life.

This was taking my love for my children to new heights.

"Wow!" Kati clicked her camera furiously. "The view is amazing!"

"Are those people down there, or ants?" Kristina said, her laughter ringing out through the woods.

"Girls, hold on!" With both arms wrapped around its mighty trunk in a bear hug, I felt the rough bark of the tree against my cheek. My heart pounded as I clung to the spruce and willed myself not to look down. "Don't stand too close to the edge."

I vaguely heard Lumberjack and Jill giving instructions to our group. Then Jack clipped his lanyard onto the pulley and, with a hearty whoop, zipped across the cable, disappearing over the trees. The group chattered excitedly, arguing over who would get to be next. I embraced the tree tighter as one by one Jill sent ecstatic explorer after ecstatic explorer flying off through the clouds.

"My turn!" I recognized Kristina's excited voice.

I uncurled one finger from the tree. "Don't you dare," my voice came out shaky and hoarse. The pounding of my heart drowned out my pathetic plea. On land, I would die for my children. Now, all my maternal instincts evaporated as I shamefully realized that if my youngest daughter wanted to take a flying leap off a tree two hundred feet up, I was too concerned about my own safety to come to her rescue. I watched with tears in my eyes as she flew through the air, clutching a cell phone, disappearing into the clouds.

"I'm next!" Kati undid her ponytail and shook her hair free. Clutching her camera in one hand, she posed for a selfie as Jill clipped her to the cable and gave her a gentle push.

"No!" I hung my head, still clinging tightly to the tree. I expected my younger, more reckless daughter to throw caution to the wind, but now my careful older one was close behind her. I hugged the tree tighter; we swayed softly in the wind, dancing to the rhythmic sounds of the forest. I inhaled its piney cologne and ran my fingers through its mossy mane.

"And last but not least!" Jill motioned for me to join her at the edge of the platform. I shook my head and tightened my grip. She reached for my hand and slowly peeled it away from the tree. I resisted, but she was remarkably strong for such a tiny woman. "You don't want to keep the others waiting, do you?"

And annoying.

"I'll just wait here until you get back," I reasoned, but she shook her head. "I know it's hard to believe, but I'm afraid of heights." I grimaced as she pulled my other arm off the trunk and slowly turned my body to face her.

"There's no turning back now." Jill spoke to me like I was a woman on the verge of a nervous breakdown. Which I was. "I'll be right behind you."

I wrung my hands as she clipped my equipment onto a pulley. I glanced back one last time at the safe spot in the shade where my tree and I had shared a warm embrace. "That thing won't hold me!"

"I think it will." Jill tugged on my harness as if to reassure me.

"I lied about my weight on the waiver!" I blurted out this shameful confession, hoping I would be banned from the park.

She gave me a once over and adjusted a strap. "We know. We added thirty pounds." Before I could open my mouth to protest, she continued, "Just straighten your legs in front of you and enjoy the view. Remember, slow down by pulling on the cable right before you reach the next platform."

I don't want to die this way! A million thoughts ran through my head. *What if they bury me in some awful dress?* I could hear it now: *What possessed her to do it? She had a beautiful life until she jumped off that tree in Alaska. Wearing some kind of kinky leather harness, no less. I heard she did it for her children. Alaska! Why'd she want to go there, anyway? It's for old people.*

I teetered on the edge of the platform making the mistake of looking down past my feet where as far as I could see was sky and trees. My heart leaped into my throat. Then Jill pushed me with demonic strength, and I flew through the air. "Nooooo!"

My anguished scream echoed through the woods. The bright warm day grew dark and chilly for a moment as my harnessed Tong-ass zipped past the sun. I imagined parents down below shielding their children's eyes from the round globes seeping out of the bottom of my harness. *Don't look directly at it!* they'd shout at the little ones. *You'll go blind!*

The wind took my breath away as I soared through the trees. I made promises to God I had no intention of keeping and recited the Lord's Prayer seven times. Then, miraculously, I spotted something in the distance. My light at the end of the tunnel appeared to me in the shape of a platform. I might survive, after all, if a branch didn't impale me first.

I squinted. I could make out the form of a man waving his arms, his mouth open as he shouted something.

As I drew nearer, I could see my daughters gesturing frantically at me, reaching up and pulling something over and over again.

"Mom, slow down!"

By the time I made the alarming realization that I was speeding toward Jack with the power of a derailed train, it was too late. The others dived behind the tree trunk for shelter as I flew full force into his spread arms.

The impact of our helmets nearly knocked me out cold. I could feel the splintered texture of the platform under my knees, but something warm and forgiving had broken my fall. I breathed in a musky, woodsy smell. Maybe my worst nightmare had turned into a pleasant dream. I would open my eyes and find I had dozed off on a beach in Hawaii, a romance novel spread open on my tanned tummy.

I tried to speak, but something furry and round gagged my mouth. The figure beneath me squirmed in an enticing way, and I almost didn't want to open my eyes.

"Mom!" Kristina's tone of disapproval was unmistakable.

My eyes flew open. To my horror, I found myself straddling Jack, whose helmet had flown off in our collision. His bite-size man bun was lodged firmly in my mouth.

"I'm okay!" he said. He brushed himself off, clambered to his feet and reshaped his bun.

Sputtering, I staggered to my feet as Kati clicked her camera feverishly. Avoiding the edge of the platform, I raced to the middle and embraced the safety of the tree. At least I was alive. And more than ready for the free hot chocolate promised in the brochure.

Just then, Jill soared up, landing gracefully on the platform. "Who's ready for zip line number two?"

The others clamored for position in line, each one wanting to be first.

"Wait a minute!" My fear echoed through the forest. "You mean we have to do this again?"

Jack turned his back to me, feigning interest in some pulleys, but Jill looked me directly in the eyes. "We have seven more zip lines," she ignored the panic on my face, "and three suspension bridges."

"Look, we signed up to zip-line, and now we've zip-lined," I reasoned with the perky blonde. "It's really not for me, and I'd like to go home." From the corner of my eye, I saw Kati and Kristina wither in unison.

"We're in the middle of the rainforest on a platform." Jill's steely gray eyes bore into mine. "There are only two ways out. You complete the course," her evil smile sent shivers up my spine, "or we lower you down on a rope. Someone will come by to pick you up in a few hours." Her eyes gleamed. "If a bear doesn't first. The choice is yours."

Still clinging to the tree, I looked down. I contemplated descending the rope of shame, getting stuck all alone, bear bait bobbing in midair, a tasty treat for the first grizzly that ambled by. How I wished I were on that boring train ride, sitting next to my parents, sipping coffee and chatting about my father's sugar level.

Jill nodded with satisfaction when she saw my indecision, then addressed the others, "This is a longer, faster zip line." She paused until the cheering stopped. "So feel free to experiment with some spins."

Jack whooshed off upside down along the cable to ready the next platform for our arrival. The girls jumped up and down in anticipation, planning how they could get the perfect shot of their stunts. My only comfort was the tree gently rocking in my arms. "It'll get better," the others promised, pumped up on adrenaline. "Don't you feel empowered now that you've faced your greatest fear?" But each zip line proved to be more humiliating than the last. In one day, I'd become an avid tree hugger. Only I wasn't saving trees; they were saving me. At each step in the course, Jill would mutter under her breath and unwrap me from my leafy embrace.

Goodbye, tall, bark, and handsome! I'll never fir-get you . . .

Ignoring my protests, she'd clip me onto the next pulley and send me hurling through the sky at breakneck speed. Jack quaked in his hiking boots each time he saw me racing toward him.

The bridges were no better. The others pretended not to enjoy making them wobble to hear my screams.

In fact, the best part of the entire day was landing on the final platform. At last, I could see the ground. My daughters cringed as I kneeled down and kissed the weathered wood. Jack presented each of us with a bronze medal for completing the course and hustled us down to the lodge gift shop.

I sat on a bench sipping hot chocolate and waiting for my knees to stop shaking while the girls shopped. A few minutes later, they walked up wearing matching knit moose caps and handed me a small paper bag.

"What's this?" I pulled out a pair of wool socks with a scene of Alaska on them, a blue glacier stretching up each leg.

"They're for you." Kati grinned. "So you'll never get cold feet again. You really faced your fears up there, Mom."

"I'm not sure which fear I was facing." I felt the texture of the wool in my hand and traced the outline of the glacier with my fingertip. "My fear of heights, or my fear of getting old; well, of seeming old to you."

I leaned down, changed into my new socks, and wiggled my toes. "Sometimes you get cold feet because you're scared, and maybe that's a good thing. It saves you from doing something dangerous." The wind picked up and I hugged myself. "And sometimes you get cold feet because it's cold."

We boarded the bus that would take us back to the ship. The girls dozed as I gazed out the window, mesmerized by the view. The very tip of the Mendenhall Glacier glistened in the distance like a blue diamond dropped straight from heaven into a crystal pool of water. The trees lining the road were lush with leaves. The bus driver pointed out an eagle soaring overhead. As we circled down the mountain, I could see the ornate caboose of an old train on the tracks below, chugging slowly through the forest.

Maybe my mom was right. A little shopping and a bus tour were all the adventure I needed. I looked forward to seeing my parents that night and sharing stories about our adventures over dinner. I closed my eyes, replaying the day in my head. I may have faced a fear, but I certainly hadn't overcome it. *That's the last time I let my kids talk me into something I don't want to do. No matter how old I am!* I nodded off to the humming of the bus motor.

An abrupt stop jolted me awake. A long line of brake lights signaled the road was closed ahead. Sirens wailed in the distance. The driver picked up the microphone and made an announcement to the passengers. "Sorry for the delay, folks. It seems the White Pass historic train has derailed. We don't know how serious it is yet, but I see lots of ambulances up ahead. We might be here awhile . . ."

I gasped and sat up straighter, trying to get a better view out the window. *Not the train I made my parents go on!* I searched in my backpack for my phone. No service. I woke up the girls, but there was nothing we could do as the bus inched its way through the traffic.

Kristina sobbed against the window, her shoulders gently shaking. "I can see the train down there!" She grabbed my hand. "It doesn't look good."

Fear and guilt consumed me as I thought of my parents in that wreckage. They would never have been there in the first place if I hadn't shamed them into going. If I hadn't made them feel old. *Take a deep breath.* I willed myself to remain positive. We didn't know where their seats were on that train. Surely not all the cars were part of that tangled mess. I gripped my armrest as the bus continued to creep along the highway.

When we finally made it to the dock, the girls and I ran all the way to the ship, barely slowing down for security. I stopped an officer at the entrance of the ship. "The train wreck! My parents . . ."

"Go to the purser's desk." He pointed to a long line snaking through the lobby. "They'll answer your questions." He noticed the panic in my eyes and softened. "There were no casualties."

We joined the others at the back of the line.

"That old couple's been up there for fifteen minutes," a red-faced man growled in front of us. "Hurry up already!"

I looked up to see what couple he was talking about and spotted my mom and dad, holding hands and two cups of coffee, walking away from the desk. "Who do you think you're calling old?" I pushed past the man and ran up to my parents. "Are you okay?"

"The damn train derailed." My dad shook his head and raised an eyebrow. "But we got them to give you a refund."

"Who cares about the refund? We were so worried about you!" The girls and I hugged the pair, careful not to spill their coffee in our excitement.

"Those poor old people!" My mother clucked her tongue. "You could never get *me* on that train. Did you see those cliffs in the brochure?"

"What do you mean?" I studied their faces, more confused than ever. "I bought you tickets."

My mother looked down, a sheepish look on her face. "Besides, Albert didn't want to wake up that early. We stayed on board and had a nice lunch on the deck." She beamed at her granddaughters. "Did you girls have a relaxing day?"

My daughters laughed at my expression, and Kati made us all pose for a picture.

"I don't know about you, but I'm hungry." My dad headed in the direction of the dining room with my mother trailing behind.

"Hey, Mom!" Kristina pointed to the excursion desk. Beside it hung a huge poster of a smiling family sitting in an inflatable raft, wearing life jackets and white knuckles. *Enjoy a heart-pounding fourteen-mile trip down Class IV whitewater rapids,* it read. *Guides are certified swift-water rescue technicians!* "What are we doing tomorrow?"

"I'm too old for that!" I made the announcement with pride and hurried to catch up with my parents. I might have been over the hill, but I wanted to live to see a few more mountains.

Suddenly my feet felt cold.

You Better Believe It

My son stared up at me, eyes large pools of dark chocolate that melted my heart. He was sitting cross-legged at the foot of our twinkling Christmas tree, wearing green plaid holiday pajama pants and an expectant grin. His white Siberian Husky sprang up and shook his fur when he saw me, spraying the freshly swept hardwood floor and most of the tree with a fine cloud of fuzz the color of snow.

"Sinbad loves Christmas!" Alston patted the dog's head and wrapped his arms around his pet's neck. "He can't wait for Santa to come."

My heart skipped a beat. As a single mom, I longed to preserve his innocence and the magic of Christmas as long as possible. But maybe this was the year to have *The Talk*. The *Santa* talk. I looked over my shoulder to make sure his younger sisters weren't around. I could hear them in another room, wrapping last minute presents, arguing about what color bows to stick on the gifts.

"Put the red one on Dad's Star Wars socks," I heard Kati command.

"That doesn't match!" Kristina insisted. There was the sound of paper tearing followed by a scream.

"Alston," I began, "about Santa…"

"We must have a *really* good family." Alston shook his head. "Or leave out the best cookies in the neighborhood." He paused and waggled his eyebrows. "Some of my friends are talking."

I held my breath.

"They don't *believe*."

I exhaled, my shoulders slumping.

He pointed to the limp red and white stockings hung in a row across the mantle, each one stitched with a family member's name in cursive. Tomorrow morning they would be too heavy to hang from a nail over the fireplace and would be displayed lovingly on the floor, stuffed to the brim with candy and tiny treasures, propped up against a mound of gifts personally chosen by Santa.

Alston continued, "They get *gift* cards. Cash, even." I nodded my head, imagining the simplicity of a house without Santa. "They sleep in on Christmas morning."

I glanced at my watch. No one in this family slept in on Christmas morning. Each year, the kids sprang from their beds at dawn and thundered into my room. "Merry Christmas, Mom! Wake up! Wake up!" With bleary eyes, I'd stumble to the kitchen to bake cinnamon rolls, then video them racing to the tree as they tore into their stockings. Somehow, each year St. Nick knew the perfect gifts to keep the thrill of Christmas alive.

But now ... it was nearly midnight and every creature was stirring that lived in this house. I had to get the kids to bed or I'd never get any sleep. I could see the girls banging around in the kitchen, waving spatulas at each other and arguing over what kind of cookies to burn first.

"Santa likes chocolate chip best." Kristina wrestled to open a bag of the semi-sweet morsels she found in the pantry until the package exploded all over the kitchen floor.

Kati squealed as she tiptoed barefoot over the pointy chocolate pieces. "Everyone knows the only real Christmas cookie is a sugar cookie. Mom, where are the red hots?"

They spent the next half hour shaking sprinkles on everything but the cookies, then decided what they really wanted was to bake and build a ginger bread house. From scratch. At midnight.

"There will be no Christmas unless all of you get to bed!" I growled like the Grinch.

My son had moved to the sofa where he huddled under a red fleece throw, softly snoring, Sinbad curled in a heap under the tree. "Alston, you know you're too heavy for me to carry you up." I shook him until he stumbled to his feet and sleep-walked up the stairs, his younger sisters, their hands sticky with colored sugar, following behind.

"Everyone go to your room, and shut the door behind you. Don't you dare come out until morning."

I sighed as I thought of the long night ahead, of the kitchen to be cleaned, the gifts to be wrapped, the lists to be made and checked— twice. Despite my weariness, I gazed at the tree glowing in the corner of the living room, my children's handmade ornaments peeking out from the branches, and my eyes twinkled with joy.

I'd made a vow years ago that despite the divorce, every December the halls would be decked down to the last red foil chocolate Hershey kiss. The family feast would be festive, the gift-giving grand. After all, a single mother had 364 other days to juggle homework and housework. For twenty-four perfect holiday hours, our home would be an idyllic scene from the inside of a snow globe that I would single-handedly shake until our world sparkled with white flurries and traditions topped with tinsel. No matter how heavy my arms grew, I wouldn't stop until the last cookie was eaten and the final gift opened and admired. Only then would I allow the powdery dust to settle on another year. It was a game we never tired of playing and we each knew our role.

Maybe next year we'd have the Santa talk. This year, the stockings were hung by the chimney (with dog hair). Christmas carols filled the air and the delicious aroma of freshly baked cookies wafted from the kitchen. I took a bite out of a chocolate chip one, then, to be fair, sampled the sugar. I placed the half-eaten cookies on a holiday plate and left it by the fireplace. Every tradition was as carefully preserved as the delicate ornaments that bobbed on the branches.

I couldn't resist wandering up the stairs to check on the children. I opened the door to Kristina's room. So caught up in the magic of the moment, I almost expected to find her snuggling her well-loved Pooh. My eyes adjusted to the dim light and I blinked.

In the shadows where a preschooler once lay, a college freshman sprawled across her bed, wearing a Texas Tech sweatshirt and ear buds. In the room next door, Kati slept peacefully, a copy of Bride magazine opened across her chest. Alston, exhausted from the long drive from his apartment in Dallas, had collapsed on his bed, a hairy leg sticking out from the bottom of his holiday pajama pants, his work laptop softly humming in the corner. As I bent down to kiss him on the forehead, it occurred to me we'd never had the Santa talk. But if we had, I'd have told him the truth— that Santa was love. And you should never stop believing in love.

I tiptoed out of his room and went downstairs to admire my handiwork. Only thing that really changed: the gifts. Lovingly laid out in three generous piles were presents from their wish lists— the latest iPhone where Playmobil once ruled, a Nikon camera and a Nintendo Wii where American Girl dolls once waited to be hugged. I smiled and made my way through the darkened house, slipped into bed and savored the silent night.

In their desperate desire to give their children a perfect Christmas experience all wrapped in a bow, single moms get overlooked sometimes. We proudly wear macaroni necklaces long after they're fashionable. We smooth fir-scented body lotion on our hands and light candles in handmade holders made with baby food jars and colored tissue. I'd discovered a long time ago that the most perfect gifts weren't the ones wrapped under the tree, they were the ones curled under the covers upstairs.

Alston was right. We have a really good family. Only that could explain how we always get just what we want— to be together.

I'd been a very good mom this year, and once again, Santa knew just what I wished for Christmas— to have my babies home for the holidays. After all, me and the big guy go back a long way.

Would I ask for the same thing again next year?

You better believe it.

Cock-a-Doodle-Do

The morning of my birthday, I limped to the bathroom mirror and examined the face staring back at me, bleary eyed and tired. Getting older was nothing to be afraid of, but my reflection certainly was. I tried to ignore the dark circles pooling under my eyes and the tiny wrinkles crinkling around them, trying to focus on the positive. A wonderful weekend awaited! I would welcome this birthday as I had the forty-nine others, celebrating with friends and family who would confirm that I was only getting better with each passing year.

My thoughts turned to what I would wear. I would need a little something for lunch with friends, a happy hour (or two) and a romantic dinner with Cowboy.

Sweet-talking Cowboy who, with his velvety voice and rugged charm, had lassoed me in, but not quite tied the knot. This could be the year, our year.

I turned to walk away and gasped. Over my shoulder, I caught a glimpse of my profile and froze. My heart pounded and I faced the mirror again. Everything seemed to be in order. I turned to the other side this time and my mouth dropped open. I tentatively touched the side of my face and pushed it up an inch, then let go. I whipped my head from side to side, viewing my face from every angle. My bottom lip trembled as I made the jaw dropping realization that somehow Father Time had crept into my bed overnight, stolen my chin, and left my puffy, pasty face currently residing on my shoulders.

Crying only made the situation worse. My face was falling, and until someone invented a push-up bra for facial cheeks, the only thing that seemed to prop it up was a huge, fake smile.

So I smiled. All day.

I smiled when my friend, Celeste, told me she was going out of town for a romantic weekend with her husband and wouldn't be available for lunch, happy hour, or to hold my face back for me as I threw up too many margaritas and memories. I smiled when my daughter informed me I never should have let my birthday fall on the same day as prom, and that she couldn't possibly have brunch with me because she had booked a hair appointment, a mani-pedi, and a pre-prom photo session with twenty of her closest friends.

I smiled when my sister reminded me that, birthday or not, she was throwing a graduation party for my nephew that afternoon and I was welcome to come.

I smiled when the man I had been dating for five years revealed he joined a gun club that very morning and would be busy shooting all day, but would try to find time for a casual dinner late that night.

When my own mother couldn't meet me for shopping because she was washing her hair, I accepted the inevitable. This was one birthday I would have to face alone. Dejected, I didn't bother changing out of my fuzzy pajamas. I turned off my phone, returned to my warm, cozy bed, and smiled myself back to sleep.

Later that afternoon I woke to a pounding on my door. "Happy Birthday, Peaches!" Cowboy cried as I cracked open the door, my foot firmly placed behind it. "Why didn't you answer your phone? I've been trying to call you. I have a big surprise!"

I was tempted to hold a grudge a little longer. After all, he'd stood me up for a gun range, but his wide country grin was hard to resist so I stood back, letting him come inside.

"Look at that big smile!" he said as he engulfed me in a huge, one-sided hug. "And I was afraid you were mad at me."

"I am mad at you," I said through clenched teeth.

"You know how much I love you," he began, taking my hand. "I've been planning this for a long time. I wanted it to be perfect. I know you like big, shiny things, and I've been shopping for just the right one. Will you..." he dropped to his knee in the middle of my kitchen, and my heart skipped a beat, "look at that! My shoe's untied again."

He stood back up, ran outside, and with an exaggerated flourish, came back carrying a huge metal red and gold yard rooster with happy birthday balloons tied around its neck. I resisted the urge to kick him in the cock-a-doodle do.

"I know we're going to your nephew's graduation party today," he continued, "but I want to take you out for your birthday after." I looked up at him expectantly. "Maybe we can grab a burger, or something."

My face froze into a steely smile. This would be the last birthday I would waste with this man. This may be how they celebrate in Nebraska, but in Texas we party until the metal rooster crows. I don't care how many things he repaired around my house. He would not be able to fix this, no matter what tool he pulled out of his belt.

Somehow, I made it through the day. I smiled as I congratulated my nephew, ate a piece of non-birthday cake, and agreed when my family suggested we celebrate my birthday real soon, like next year. I smiled until

Cowboy and I were the last ones at the party and my cheeks were sore from overexertion.

"I hope you don't mind, but I have one stop to make before we get something to eat," said Cowboy as we settled into the car. "A customer wants me to give him a bid on a restaurant renovation."

My shoulders drooped, I relaxed my face, tense from hours of false bravado. *Chin up*, I said to myself, then remembered I no longer had one. The day could not possibly get any worse.

We pulled in to Uptown Park and started walking towards a collection of boutiques and restaurants. Cowboy paused, confusion shadowing his face. "Wait here, baby, while I run in to see if this is the right place."

I sat on the ledge of a fountain clutching my purse as a group of twenty-something punks walk past, eying me, each with one hand on his cell phone and one holding up the seat of his pants. It would be just my luck to be mugged on my birthday and shoved into the fountain while Cowboy ambled aimlessly from shop to shop. I could see it now on the ten o'clock news: *Fifty-something divorcee pulled from depths of Uptown Park fountain, suffering lacerations to the face and a severe concussion. Her maniacal smile led officials to suspect drugs are involved.*

The hairs on the back of my neck sprang to attention as a late model black Cadillac with darkened windows slowed to a stop at the curb and the door sprang open, loud music booming from within. Just when I had convinced myself I was about to be the target of a kidnapping, or worse, I recognized a Bruno Mars song. Suddenly the twenty-something's broke out into dance, spinning and gyrating in unison to the beat of *Marry You* blasting in the air. I breathed a sigh of relief as I spotted a young girl smiling beside me and realized there was nothing to fear. I was witnessing a flash mob! Some rapper's girlfriend was clearly getting a proposal she could not refuse. At least someone's day was going better than mine.

I longed for her youth, the anything-is-possible expression in her eyes, the defiant thrust of her chin. I envied the decades of happily ever after she had ahead of her, the birthdays to be celebrated instead of feared.

I looked up and saw a red-haired figure in the distance walking towards me from one of the restaurants. My heart soared. Celeste had said she was out of town, but here she was, laughing at the confused expression on my face. Before I had time to think, my daughter emerged from behind her, cutting prom weekend short. Then they all appeared, one by one, grinning from ear to ear, and when all my family and friends had gathered around me, Cowboy walked through them, holding a huge bouquet of flowers and my heart.

He got down on one knee. This time it was not to tie his shoe.

I nodded yes, pulled him close, and broke out into my first genuine smile of the weekend. The big cock may have been from Buccee's convenience store, but the big rock was not. Suddenly the future was bright.

I would not have to face it alone.

Of Mice & Women

Summer officially arrived the day my younger daughter, Kristina, came home from college dragging a semester's worth of dirty clothes behind her. She wanted home cooked meals and movie marathons on the sofa, soul searching conversations and the chance to sleep late in her childhood room. It was also the same day my husband went out of town for work and I leaped at the rare opportunity to give my youngest my undivided attention, to be a mother again.

She plopped down overstuffed bags looking around wide-eyed, as if seeing our home for the very first time. "It looks so big!" She ran her fingertip across the countertop. "And clean. My roommates are pigs!" She skipped over to the pantry and flung open the door. "Do we have anything to eat? I'm starving!" Her eyes lit up when she saw all her favorite snacks lovingly displayed on the pantry shelves. "Thanks, Mom!" She pulled out a bag of Oreos and tore into the package. "There's no place like home."

My heart filled with joy. I couldn't wait to feather my empty nest again. We listened to Motown and cooked her favorite dinner, talking long into the night about her hopes and dreams. We binge watched *Shameless* on Netflix, horrified and amused by the dysfunctional Irish family living in squalor. Finally, we drifted off to sleep secure and safe on matching sofas. Home sweet home.

The mommy-moon ended the next day when I stumbled into the kitchen to make coffee. Still bleary-eyed with sleep, I reached into the breadbasket for English muffins. *Unbelievable! She's no better than her roommates.* I held up the package in disgust. Instead of untwisting the tie like a civilized person, my ragamuffin of a daughter in a carb frenzy had torn open the bag from the bottom and grabbed a fist full, leaving smushed gnarly remains behind. "Kristina!" I yelled at the sleeping form on the couch. "Did you do this? You might live like this in college, but at home we don't act like animals!"

My daughter slunk into the kitchen with a scowl on her face. "What are you talking about? I didn't do that! Besides, I like bagels better." She dug around the breadbasket for a brand-new bag of Everything bagels I'd bought just for her, pointed to a huge hunk torn out of the side of the package, and glared at me accusingly. "Really Mom? I thought these were for me!"

It was then we heard a rustling from the darkest corner of the pantry followed by the tiniest of squeals. We dropped our baked goods, screamed in unison and dove at the pantry door, slamming it shut.

"Mom! Do something!" Kristina was already frantically scrolling down the screen of her phone. She thrust it at me.

The Orkin lady who answered was painfully calm, no doubt from years of dealing with hysterical women. "What makes you think you have a rodent issue? Have you seen droppings?"

"No, I haven't seen droppings." I flung open cabinets with my free hand, searching for a sign of an infestation, not wanting to find one. I threw the muffins and bagels into the trash, repulsed at the sight of them. "But something is squeaking and has attacked our bread!"

"Let me see." Her tone was unconcerned, like a woman who had all the time in the world and kept her bread products in the refrigerator. "How about next..." her voice paused as I glared at the cell phone, "Thursday?"

From the corner of my eye, I saw a flicker of movement from under the pantry door. I screamed in response, "This is an emergency!"

Kristina and I sat on the kitchen table. She threatened to move back to Lubbock while I left manic messages on my husband's phone. Finally, after what seemed like hours, the doorbell rang and I ran to the entrance, never happier to have a visitor, even if he was carrying a clipboard.

I needed a hero. I needed Hercules with poison pellets and steel traps to purge my home of the pests within.

Instead, I got Willard.

Reading the name on his starched white shirt I examined the man before me. His skin was mousy brown and his nose twitched slightly as he looked up at me. I outweighed him by at least fifty pounds. "May I come in?" he spoke with a mild stutter and had already slipped blue paper booties over his shoes.

My heart sank. This man couldn't kill a fly. I felt the need to protect him, to feed him, but then I remembered I was never going into my pantry again. I told him about my bread and he shook his head. "Don't you worry. These things happen. We're going to take good care of you." He disappeared into the pantry and shut the door behind him.

Kristina and I returned to our perch on the table, trying to ignore the crashing coming from behind the pantry door. "I'm staying at Emma's tonight," she informed me.

Willard emerged, a triumphant look on his face. "I found some droppings. They're large so I think we're looking at more than mice here." He pointed to a collection of brown morsels on the pantry floor.

"I thought those were Oreo crumbs," mumbled Kristina.

I leaned my head down as far as I dared. "They look like chocolate chips to me."

Before I knew it, Willard was in the utility room pulling the dryer out from the wall. "We have to figure out where they're getting in."

I watched in horror as he squeezed himself into the tiny space behind the dryer where all the lost thongs live. The humiliation was too great. I leaned over to Kristina and whispered in her ear, "If he asks, we're telling him we're house sitting for a neighbor, got that?"

Seconds later he called out to us, "Here's where they're getting in." He pointed to a pile of droppings on the floor next to a lacy black pair of panties. "Mice are stupid, but rats are smart." Willard crammed wire mesh into this hole he found by the vent. "We have to trick them into coming into our traps." He held up a small white sticky board. "When they try to get out, this trap will stop them in their tracks."

I mentally compared the paper-thin piece of cardboard he held to the bite mark on the bagel. This flimsy film of flypaper wouldn't stop a flea, much less what I was sure was a raccoon size creature in my pantry. It was like no mousetrap I'd ever seen. When I was younger, I remember my dad putting a Cheeto on a contraption that would snap a mouse's head and kill him dead. But that was in an era when husbands didn't travel and the world hadn't decided to build a new and improved way of solving an age-old problem.

Kristina poked her head behind the dryer. "I don't get it. How does that kill the rat?"

Willard hung his head as if he hated this part of his job. "It doesn't kill it. The rat gets stuck on it."

"Then what?" I demanded. I cursed my husband under my breath. Where was he when I needed him? No doubt living it up at some Holiday Inn bar while my daughter and I battled Bubonic plague at home.

Willard looked up at me, eyes full of emotion. "Then you call me. I'll give you my direct number. I'll come back and..." he hesitated and lowered his voice, "dispose of it for you."

His calmness was contagious. I trusted the little man and allowed him to hide thirteen traps throughout my home. He made his way up the stairs, pausing every now and then to scoop something up into his gloved hand. "Droppings," he pronounced.

"All this time I thought my carpet had black specks on it."

"Your carpet's white."

I walked him to the door and fought the urge to embrace him. Gone was the timid man who entered my home an hour ago. In his place stood a confident killer. *Don't leave me to run this rat race alone! Stay! I'm really not a bad housekeeper.*

He paused on the porch and handed me his card. "Call me anytime. Except Sunday. I don't work Sundays."

I felt flushed as I watched him swagger out to his van; I imagined he was on his way to rescue another damsel in distress. His skin took on a bronze tone in the sun and I watched the bulge of a bicep as he pulled a pair of dark sunglasses out of his pocket and put them on. Before my eyes he transformed from a mild-mannered mouse catcher to the Ex-Terminator. He turned to me, his voice dropped an octave as he spoke, "I'll be back."

I almost felt sorry for the rats.

A long weekend dodging droppings and dying rats was not what I had in mind for Kristina's first few days of summer. Still, I was thankful to not have to face the rodents alone. My daughter would give me moral support and a strong shoulder to scream on if the nasty little creatures decided to brave the light of day. We would get through this tough time like families do, together.

Just then, Kristina came barreling out of the house holding a duffel bag. "I'm out of here!" She waved at me as she hurried to her car calling over her shoulder, "Sorry, Mom, but I didn't sign up for this." She threw her bag in the backseat, jumped behind the wheel and screeched off before I could beg her to stay.

I forced myself to go back inside. *What are you, a mom or a mouse?* It would be dark soon and the party in the pantry would be in full swing. But this was my house, after all, and this roach hotel had a No Vacancy sign. It would take more than a tiny little mouse problem to scare me out of my own home.

First, I would make myself something to eat. I tiptoed to the kitchen so I wouldn't wake any mice and stared at the pantry door. Cookies and crackers and chips called my name. I heard a faint rustling from inside. Suddenly, I wasn't hungry anymore.

Woman loses 30 pounds in one night by cutting carbs on the new Ratkins Diet. Call your exterminator for details. I settled for a bottle of water from the fridge and went into the family room. I figured a little *Shameless* would help me forget my own problems so I settled onto the sofa, tucking my feet up under me to be safe.

In the middle of episode five, my husband called. "So, how's the rat problem?"

I rolled my eyes. The carefree sound of his voice grated on my last nerve. "Come home and find out, if you're so concerned."

He poked the bear. "I've been telling you for years to get rid of the clutter."

I cut him off, "Good night! Sleep tight." How dare he insinuate the furry little things had invaded just to nestle in my collection of old magazines and bags of slightly too small clothes. *Hope the bed bugs bite!* I was considering hurling my phone across the room when I got a text from a number I didn't recognize.

Just wanted to check on you. How are things at the house?

Suspicious, I typed back. *Who is this?*
Willard.

Willard? I sat up straighter and fluffed my hair.
Have you heard anything?

I smiled to myself. *Not a creature is stirring* I texted. What kind of woman flirts with her exterminator? I was as shameless as the TV characters and just as desperate.

Around midnight I turned off the TV. Clearly, I was worried about nothing. The little incident in the pantry was an isolated event and my fears were foolish. It was time for bed and I rose from the couch.

Then I heard it! The domino effect started with a thumping in the pantry, followed by a crash. Then a metallic clang rang out from the utility room, like something was caught in the tiny space behind the washer and dryer. Upstairs in the loft something dragged across the carpet, trapped and frantic. The squealing and screeching of tortured rats almost drowned out my screams. These were sounds of Nutcracker proportion and I envisioned man-sized mice wielding swords, fighting for their lives. I ran to my bedroom, slammed the door and stuffed a bath towel under it.

Willard! I punched his number into my phone. *Willard?* I held my breath, waiting for a response, but there was no answer. I looked at the time on my phone. 12:06am. **Sunday!** Willard's only day off.

I got into bed, covered my head with my blanket and squeezed my eyes shut. Somehow, I got through the night. The next morning with the sun streaming into my bedroom window, I could almost believe the night before was just a dream. I put on shoes, crept across the room and put my ear against the door. Silence. I cracked the door open and waited. Stillness. I went into the kitchen to investigate.

I glared at the pantry door. *It's time to face your fears, pack-rat to rat-pack.* I grabbed a carving knife from the wooden block and inched open the door. Not a mouse was in sight, but at my feet laid one of Willard's white sticky boards, stained and covered with droppings. The message was loud and clear. *Stick this in your trap, lady!*

Willard said he'd never seen such a sight in his life, and he's been in the business for 30 years. He'd also never worked a Sunday before but he showed up in his church clothes and discreetly disposed of five unwelcome guests. Three perished behind the dryer, the blind leading the blind in a futile escape. One met its maker upstairs near a pile of Kristina's unwashed laundry. Finally, the overweight ringleader that masterminded the invasion was stabbed to death in the dark corner of the pantry. Willard said he was missing his tail.

I signed a ten-year contract with Willard and we text often between visits, just to keep in touch. We've grown to be friends as people often do when they've shared a traumatic event. In fact, I'm inviting him over for Thanksgiving dinner.

I can't wait for him to meet my husband.

He's been a real pest lately.

Pomp & Circumstances

My daughter's college graduation day would be picture perfect if it killed me.

I started preparing for battle months ago, sending out announcements to family and friends, begging the university for extra tickets so that our extended family could attend. My job entailed printing out maps, arranging transportation and coordinating drivers. I arranged for everyone to meet at our house to caravan so no one would get lost or be tempted to wander off for an impromptu breakfast. I bribed the bunch with brunch after the ceremony at the only restaurant in town taking reservations on graduation day if they would only show up on time.

Clueless about the number of all-nighters that went into pulling off an event of this magnitude, my new husband, who I affectionately nicknamed Cowboy, wandered into the kitchen the morning of graduation and caught me bedazzling *Gig 'Em* (the Texas A&M rendition of get 'em) on the top of Kati's graduation cap with rhinestone and glitter. "Why did you wait until the last minute?" he asked.

I wanted to hot glue his mouth shut.

Before I could comment, Kati flew into the kitchen, hair still wet from her shower, holding two different shoes and wearing her seventh dress of the morning. "How's this one?" She spun around in a circle, her skirt fluttering up in an arc above her knees. "And which shoes? The pumps or the flats?"

I wanted to remind her no one would even see her dress or shoes under the long gown I'd ironed at 4:30 that morning, that today she would stand out for her accomplishments, not her appearance. I longed to hug her and hold back time, to keep her mine for a little longer. Instead, I examined her outfit and wisely nodded my head. "Perfect!"

She ignored me and waved at her head with a Kate Spade pump. "And my hair's a mess!" she wailed. "I hate Houston humidity!"

The doorbell rang, signaling the first of our entourage had arrived. Kati stormed up the stairs to finish dressing. I answered the door; family members dragged in, still bleary eyed.

"I don't understand why they have to have the graduation so early!" My dad and a heavy splash of Old Spice greeted me with a hug.

My mother followed behind carrying a small cooler of diabetes medicine for my dad and a donut shaped pillow for herself, prepared for the four-hour ceremony. She patted his beefy arm. "Now Albert, this is once in a lifetime. We can wake up a little early for such an important day."

"Wake up?" My younger brother filed in behind them with my aunt and cousin. "I didn't even bother going to sleep last night."

I handed out steaming cups of coffee in to-go containers. If I'd known the Herculean effort it was going to take to get my daughter and her biggest fans to the early morning graduation ceremony on time, I might have suggested she attend an online college and have her diploma conveniently mailed to our doorstep.

"There's no time to talk." I yelled for Kati to hurry and threatened her brother and sister they wouldn't live to see their own graduations if they didn't get out of bed this very instant. I ushered everyone back outside, assigning them to cars. We were on the road to College Station at exactly 6:30am. Fifteen minutes later, we slowed down at a Bucc-ees long enough to allow my ex-husband's truck to slide into the tail end of our convoy. I waved at his new girlfriend through the window. *This alone should earn me a Masters in Motherhood.*

An hour later we screeched to a stop in front of Reed Arena. Kati bolted from the car, maroon gown billowing behind her as she hurried to meet the other graduates already lined up at the entrance. She fluffed her long brown curls and slapped a bling-topped mortarboard onto her head.

"Just get some decent photos!" she called to me over her shoulder.

I cringed. It was a fair warning to the mom who had once recorded an entire ballet recital with the lens cap still on. "Of course! Good luck, Kati...I love you!" My breath caught as I watched her figure merge into a sea of maroon. She was racing towards a future that barely included me. Already she had started a new wedding photography business. Already a diamond engagement ring glinted on her left hand. Soon I would be demoted to a weekly lunch companion, trying desperately to catch up over salads at Zoe's Kitchen.

But for this momentous day, I would be the perfect mom.

We parked in the last few spaces left in the crowded lot and I leaped out of the car. The suffocating College Station air hit me like a warm, wet sponge. Ignoring the others who were stretching and moaning about the heat, I focused on my next challenge, finding us seats with the best view so I could single-handedly capture my daughter's perfect 4.0 figure as it floated across the stage.

I opened the trunk and reached for the first item, a Nikon Coolpix P500. I draped the freshly charged digital camera, loaded with a 64gb memory card, around my neck for easy access. I hoisted my bulky camcorder bag from the car, feeling the satisfying heft of the 90's video camera in my hands, and slung it over my shoulder. *They don't make them like this anymore.* In my front pocket I carried a fully loaded iPhone 6 equipped with unlimited data and a cumulus iCloud for storage, ready to draw it at the slightest provocation.

Armed and ready, I squared my shoulders, put my hands on my hips and squinted into the sun. No precious moment would go unrecorded with Techno Mom in charge. I hustled everyone together marching us single file to the arena, only slowing long enough for Kati's fiancé and his mother to hastily greet us and join our line.

"We should have stopped for breakfast," my dad grumbled as he shuffled towards the entrance.

My mother handed him a mushed granola bar from the bottom of her purse. "We'll eat later. The important thing is we're all here to see Kati graduate." She looked at me and smiled. "With honors."

Chaos reigned in the packed arena. I almost cried when we discovered the entire lower level was filled with anxious Aggies who must have camped out overnight or bribed a custodian for every prime spot. We ascended the narrow stairs to the next tier where not one empty seat remained. The air thinned as we trudged up yet another set of stairs and finally found a dozen seats together with a partially obstructed view of the stage.

I plopped into a seat in the middle of the row and fanned myself with an embossed commencement program, the camera around my neck rising and falling as I fought to catch my breath. Family flanked both sides of me. My future son-in-law and his mother settled behind us to watch the show. Our seats were far from perfect, but we were all here and that was all that mattered ... almost.

Besides that, the greatest gift I could give my photographer daughter was a perfect picture of her receiving her diploma. This required precision timing since the magical moment would be gone in a flash. There would be no retake and the burden of this responsibility rested entirely on me.

I glanced at my mother sitting at the end of the row and called over to her, "Did we even *own* a camera when I was growing up?" I was only half kidding. I didn't recall seeing a single shot of any childhood milestones. In fact, there were only two pictures of me displayed in my parents' home. One was a red-tinged Sear's photo of me posed awkwardly in front of a tired backdrop wearing a gap-toothed smile, bell bottoms, and horrible haircut. The other, a bridal portrait from my first wedding, showcased me with a tight perm wearing a white bridal gown with balloon sleeves larger than my softly smiling face.

"Did you even *take* photos at my graduation?"

"Of course, we did." She sniffed. "It was 1985, not the stone ages."

My ex's girlfriend overheard us. "They had cameras then," she volunteered. "That was the year I was born."

The first solemn notes of *Pomp and Circumstance* reverberated through the arena and I sprang to attention, clutching the camera hanging at my chest.

"It won't be long now." I craned my head, squinting to find Kati in the long line of ant-size graduates marching in to the beat. Every time I thought I caught a glimpse of her, she disappeared again. I grew frantic. "Can anyone see her?" The students all looked alike from this altitude; I got dizzy from the searching.

My husband focused his hunter's eyes on the crowd and scoped out his prey. "There she is." He pointed to the swarming mass below. "Fifth row, 13 from the right." He waved his hand and miraculously, Kati turned her head towards us. "There's no mistaking that hair."

I zoomed in on her across the thousands of parents and students gathered between us. Time seemed to stand still as she smiled and waved. My heart melted as I struggled to read her lips. *I love you, Mom,* I imagined her saying. *I couldn't have done this without you.* I clicked furiously at my camera, catching the sparkle of her cap, recording the toss of her head, her smile as she fluffed her signature curls into place.

I imagined ten years from now holding a tiny, curly haired girl on my lap, leafing through a leather-bound photo album, pointing to a picture. "That's your mother," I would say. "Isn't she beautiful? And so smart! See all the cords around her neck? What's that? Oh no, honey. You won't find a picture of grandma's graduation in this book. Cameras weren't invented in 1985."

The university president's booming voice interrupted my daydream and I tried to concentrate on his canned message. My head began to nod as he droned on about futures and journeys and new beginnings. *You'll miss one 100% of the shots you don't take.* I woke with a start and clicked away again with my camera in the general direction of Kati.

Hours seemed to pass. An endless stream of graduates crossing the tiny stage below was hypnotizing. My family on either side had glazed expressions on their faces. If there wasn't an intermission with snacks and naptime soon, I'd have a mutiny on my hands.

"Not much longer," I announced to the fading fan club; no one seemed to notice. My son and ex were engrossed in a video game on their phones. My younger daughter was busy taking selfies of her bored face and Cowboy was snoring. Only my parents listened patiently to the long list of names being called, but that was probably because their butts were numb from the hard seats and their combined sugar levels had reached an all-time low.

Finally Kati's name drew near.

"Just 10 more!" I alerted everyone and switched on my camera and camcorder.

"Five more!" I whipped my cell phone out of my pocket.

"She's next!" Tears poured down my face as I snapped and clicked and flashed, catching her momentous walk across the stage, oblivious to everything but the familiar sway of her hips, the unmistakable bounce of her waist long curls, the confident tilt of her chin. She shook the president's hand, reached for her diploma and exited the stage with grace as the crowd went wild; jumping, whooping and applauding her accomplishments.

In the click of a shutter, it was over.

I collapsed in an emotional heap, satisfied and spent. Never mind that half of us were asleep, I had managed to get everyone and her grandmother there to cheer Kati across the stage, and recorded the historical event for prosperity. My motherhood magnum opus.

Minutes later we gathered our things and filed out of the arena. The glare of the blazing Texas sun greeted us as we found our new graduate.

"Kati!" I hugged her tight, inhaling her perfume and the sweet smell of success. "I'm so proud of you! I took a ton of pictures." I was still floating on a cloud of parental pride when my daughter's future mother-in-law touched my arm.

"Congratulations!" She gave me a hug and lowered her voice, "It's such a shame your parents didn't get to see Kati get her diploma."

I froze. "What?"

"They got up right before she walked across the stage. Said they were hungry or something." She took advantage of my momentary paralysis to pose the others in a huddle around me. "Say cheese!"

My mouth opened in a silent scream. Still in shock, I approached my mother as we headed to our cars. "Tell me it isn't true."

She looked up at me, a sheepish look on her face. "Albert was hungry. He saw some people with hot pretzels and went to find the concession stand." Her shoulders sagged. "I got worried about him when he didn't come back and went to look for him. I feel terrible we missed Kati! I hope you got a good photo."

My dad shrugged and smiled. "There was a long line." A spot of mustard dotted the corner of his mouth. He held up a white sack stuffed with salty swirls. "Want one?"

We walked the rest of the way in silence. I tried to shrug it off. After all, Kati would never know they didn't see her walk across the stage. She'd remember how both her grandparents were at her graduation to show their love and support. But I knew. Memories of the award ceremonies, recitals and school programs my dad couldn't attend because of work followed me to the car. He'd missed so many special moments. I hadn't wanted them to miss this one.

I got into the passenger side and slumped against the door clutching my camera. The only thing that could cheer me up at this point was knowing I got the perfect shot, one that would live in infamy long after I was gone. I began scrolling through the thousands of photos I took of the graduation.

I passed through dozens of blurry shots, dark ones, light ones, photos of my thumb, my lap, the ceiling and floor. There were hundreds of Kati's hair from behind, her signature long locks highlighted under the fluorescent lights. Manic, I scrolled faster, until I reached a succession of distant ones of her approaching the stage, climbing the stairs, holding out her hand.

I took a deep breath, afraid to look at the next photo, the jewel of the cap and gown. I enlarged the image until I could make out the features on her face.

And screamed.

"Mom, what is it?" Kati leaned over my shoulder. "Did you get a good one?"

I waved her away, not believing what I saw on the screen. A perfectly posed bearded young man with long curly brown hair smiled straight into my camera as he reached for his diploma, his Gig 'Em cap gleaming under the lights.

All I could do was delete and repeat. Each photo, every photo from the entire, excruciating day was of a hippie haired honor student, one letter away from sharing our last name, the only boy at the agricultural school not sporting a crew cut. I frantically trashed all but the photos of the young man's back view.

Kati grabbed the camera from my hands. "Let me see!"

I held my breath.

She studied the screen, squinted and tilted her head. "Not bad, Mom. Kind of artsy how you captured me from behind." She zoomed in closer and patted her head. "I was actually having a good hair day."

We pulled up to the restaurant and sat for a few minutes in the parking lot, waiting for the others. I removed my camcorder from its bag, powered it on and smiled as it whirred to life. *This time, at least, I didn't leave the lens cap on!* I watched a few seconds of the president's speech, then the picture flitted violently from left to right, zeroed in on the crowd of graduates, then focused on the floor until it came to a heartbreaking stop.

End of tape.

"I'm not hungry, anymore," I said to no one in particular.

The other cars pulled up beside us and we got out. Kati ran up to her fiancé, grasped his hand, and the two led us into the restaurant.

"Come on Mom," she called to me over her shoulder. "We have to start planning the wedding! It's going to be perfect." She beamed. "Just like today."

The hostess led us to the private room I'd reserved. Fresh flowers and chilled mimosas greeted us; soft music played in the background. Everyone who loved Kati gathered around to toast her on her special day.

I took a long swig of champagne and smiled. A wedding! I could envision it now. Kati all in lace and

pearls, her hair cascading down under my vintage veil.
Dinner and dancing, a jazz band, candlelight.

It would be picture perfect if it killed me.

I Do Times Two

Every mother dreams of planning the perfect wedding. Long before a nervous groom-to-be slips that sparkly carat onto his hopeful bride's ring finger, a vision exists in a mother's mind of a wedding day more flawless than the diamond itself. After all, she's spent years attending weddings, leafing through bridal magazines and mentally filing away ideas, designing everything from the flowers to the food to how to cut short the embarrassing toast Uncle Nick's going to give after one too many.

I, too, thought I'd be prepared when the day finally came, but when my blushing young daughter, Kati, surprised me after lunch by pulling up to Wedding Dresses by Wilhemina, the most exclusive bridal boutique in Houston, anxiety overtook me and all my plans fluttered to the floor; crushed and forgotten like the petals from a flower girl's basket. I looked at my daughter and shook my head.

She nodded saying, "It's time, Mom."

The church, the venue, the band swirled around in my head like blurred bits of confetti fluttering just out of my grasp. I stared at the mannequin in the window, looking down demurely, dressed in a long satin gown and matching cathedral length veil, and I froze. I glanced at my daughter. At that moment, only one thing was perfectly clear. This was one bride who wouldn't be wearing white.

Kati pulled my hand excitedly as we reached the entrance, almost causing me to tumble into the softly lit shop. Frank Sinatra gently crooned in the background and the muffled murmur of female voices could be heard from behind heavy velvet curtains. The sale clerk's eyes lit up when she spotted my daughter's fresh smiling face and the well-worn Louis Vuitton I clutched under my arm. She smoothed her pencil skirt and clicked over to us on stiletto heels, eager for a sale. Rubbing her hands together, she zeroed in on my daughter, glancing at the engagement ring glittering on her left hand.

"You'll be a beautiful bride!" she gushed. "That long curly hair, your porcelain skin..." She pointed a French manicured finger at Kati and squinted. "I see you in a classic princess ball gown." A wrinkle of doubt crossed her face and she placed her hands on my daughter's slim hips. "But it's a shame to hide that gorgeous figure. Perhaps a mermaid style would be best."

Before we could answer, she put a protective arm around Kati's shoulders and whisked her into the sanctuary of the adjacent room. I followed behind like Cinderella's ugly stepsister. Tufts of tulle and satin from eggshell to ecru hung from padded hangers along the walls, beaded bodices bobbed and bowed as we walked by. Shoppers sipped champagne from crystal flutes as they fingered fine lace.

"Of course, these sample gowns will swallow you up." The saleswoman smiled at Kati, pulled several from the rack and draped them across her arm. "But any of the gowns can be custom ordered to fit."

I cleared my throat. Kati squirmed uneasily.

The sales clerk sensed our discomfort and lowered her voice. "Don't you worry about the price. We have an excellent finance plan for young brides on a budget."

I placed a hand on her arm. "You don't understand. We're not shopping for a dress for my daughter."

She took a step back, eyed me with suspicion and hugged the gowns to her ample chest.

I swallowed. "We're shopping for a dress for me."

"Oh!" She caught her breath. Despite all the Botox, a horrified expression surfaced on her face and she looked at me as if for the first time, her expert eyes sizing me up from head to toe. "You?" She regained composure and gushed, "How *wonderful*. A second chance."

Kati plucked a beaded ball gown off her arm and led me to the dressing rooms. "We'll start with this one."

The salesclerk grabbed a pair of nude Spanx off a shelf and raced after us, her heels slipping on the slick marble floor. "Let me help you!" she shouted, waving the industrial strength undergarment in the air. "That's delicate Chantilly lace. And it doesn't stretch!"

I shot her a death glare as Kati shoved me inside the dressing room and firmly shut the door. Slumping onto a rose-colored velvet stool, I examined my reflection in the softly lit mirror as Etta James' sultry voice belted out *At Last*. On a good day, I looked nice enough, almost attractive, in one of the dark-colored, swing-dresses stylish women my age wore to conceal a lifetime of gravity and gravy. I could work magic with lipstick and bold necklaces and caramel-colored highlights. But today was not a good day. Kati and the sales woman whispered in hushed tones on the other side of the door.

"Mom?" Kati's calm voice could sooth the most brazen bridezilla. "We're going to bring you some gowns that will flatter your figure. Ok?"

I raised my eyebrow at my reflection. "I guess. But no one comes in here."

I heard more whispering, then the pair of Spanx shot under the door, landing in a Lycra puddle at my feet. I reached down and scooped up the unmentionable with two fingers, dangling it in front of my waist. Stiff and unyielding, the size of one of my biceps and the color of an old Ace bandage, it seemed as out of place in this lacy, ethereal environment as I was. But the label bragged these skinny britches would smooth and sculpt my assets from ribcage to kneecap. I figured I had nothing to lose except for the inches and pounds I carried on my hips like squirming toddlers, and the peri-menopausal margarita bloat on my once flat abs.

I slipped a foot into each leg and the unforgiving undergarment slithered up as far as my ankle where it wedged tightly, refusing to budge. I stretched the leg openings and tugged until the beast swallowed up my calves then stopped to hug my pale, quivering thighs. I huffed and strained, sweat pouring down my flushed body, until I coaxed the wicked waistband half-way up my legs, where it immobilized me, cutting off my circulation as it strangled my lower limbs. This was not my granny's girdle. I panted before trying to tackle my ample derriere.

"Take this, you Lycra loving Lucifer!" I growled and pulled with all my might. For one terrifying moment, my stomach popped over the waistband like biscuits from a Pillsbury can, until the merciless monster, with a sickening sound, popped into place.

I studied my reflection in the mirror. I looked like I'd been to hell and back, or at least planned, organized and paid for my own wedding. My chest heaved from exertion, black rivulets of mascara ran down my flushed cheeks and my hair frizzed in an unbride-like coif around my head. I couldn't sit down, much less breathe. I turned sideways to see my profile, then strained to see the back view. The ugly, flesh-colored foundation encased my lower body like summer sausage. I shimmied my hips and envisioned my groom's horrified face on our wedding night when I slipped out of my white satin beaded sheath, slowly rolling down the Spanx, inch by inch, freeing folds of unfettered flesh for his pleasure.

But I'll be damned if I didn't look 15 pounds slimmer.

"Whatever you do, do not try on that lace gown hanging on the door!" the salesclerk hissed. "It's a Monique Lhuillier, and it's a size six."

It was too late. I was too vain to swap out my rose colored glasses for a sensible pair of readers from the Dollar Store. Otherwise I might not have misread the size. Or the price. What I thought was an affordable $350.00 size sixteen wedding dress I was pulling over my head and currently trying to stuff two of my assets into, was in reality a $3,500.00 size six designer creation.

Luckily, someone was uncorking another bottle of champagne and no one heard the ripping sound echoing through my dressing room.

"*Uhm*, Kati? Can you come in here for a minute, please?" I hoped she could hear my muffled plea through the heavily beaded fabric that was imprisoning my face and most of my upper torso. I heard the heavy velvet curtains swish open.

"Isn't this fun? We were just looking for some more gowns for—" My daughter gasped. "Mom! What have you done?"

"Just get me *out* of here!" I whispered fiercely.

Kati spun me around to face her. She bent my body forward and twisted the fabric, struggling to maneuver it over my head. "It's really stuck. Just let me get the salesclerk. I'm sure she can help you."

"No!" I stomped my foot. "Work it back and forth while I wiggle my shoulders." I contorted my upper body while she tugged on the tulle.

"I'm afraid it's going to..."

R-i-i-i-p! Even with my ears covered by yards of fabric, I could hear the tearing sound reverberating through the room. Kati faked a coughing fit a moment too late.

"Is everything alright in there?" the salesclerk's shrill voice floated over the curtain.

I froze.

"Oh, yes!" Kati sang out. "My mom's just feeling a little..." she paused and settled on, "*emotional.*" The dress sprang off my head and collapsed into a lake of lace on the floor, like a bridesmaid who'd had one too many at the reception. Kati and I danced a happy *kalamatiano* around the dressing room.

"Of course," replied the salesclerk. She thrust an ivory ball gown through the curtains. "Perhaps this one will work. It will—disguise—your trouble spots." An ecru sheath followed. "Or this one. Of course, they can all be altered. Our seamstress is in house."

I picked up the torn Lluillier from the floor, hung it back on its padded silk hanger and placed it in my daughter's hands.

"I'll slip this to the seamstress," Kati whispered, disappearing with the dress.

For the next excruciating hour, I tried on every style of dress Wilhemina's had to offer. The Mermaid was all washed up, the Empire crumbled and the Trumpet hit the wrong note. For better or for worse, I stepped into the billowy ball gown and tried to keep an open mind as I studied myself in the mirror. From the waist up, I was a princess in a beautiful beaded bodice that softly hugged my upper body, accentuating my décolletage. But the honeymoon ended where the enormous skirt hit my hips and tufts of tulle exploded in a six-foot circumference around my body, taking up every inch of the dressing room floor.

"Mom, are you coming out?" Kati called to me. "We want to see!"

I cringed, flattened the parachute-sized skirt as best I could, and squeezed out of the opening of the dressing room, stepping up onto a tiny platform surrounded by mirrors to model the monstrous frock.

A hush fell over the boutique. Mothers and daughters stopped shopping to stare openly at me, one of them gasped and clutched her chest. "Oh!" The sales clerk fanned herself and looked away.

Kati's eyes grew big but she regained her composure. "Okaaay. What do *you* think, Mom?"

I think I look like one of those crocheted dolls crafty old ladies use to hide their toilet paper rolls. I think if I carried a shepherd's hook instead of a bouquet down the aisle, I could pass for Little Bo Peep's big sister. I fluffed out the skirt, amazed at the sheer volume of it. *I think you could throw a surprise lingerie bridal shower for me under this dress and I'd never know it.* "I think I'll pass."

"Whew!" the salesclerk exhaled loudly and plopped down onto an overstuffed divan.

By the time I emerged from the dressing room wearing the next dress, Kati was buzzed on champagne. She was on a first name basis with her new best friend, our salesclerk, Willie, who also happened to be the owner of Wedding Dresses by Wilhemina. Willie, who had kicked off her heels and was wearing a sparkly diamond tiara on her head, had put up the Sorry We're Closed sign and was indulging as well, taking unladylike chugs straight from the bottle.

I spun in a circle for them and shrugged, the three-way mirror capturing the simplicity of the sweetheart neckline, the subtle swirl of the lace skirt as it skimmed effortlessly over my body, landing in a perfect puddle at my feet.

"That's the one!" Kati jumped up, almost spilling her champagne.

"Bravo!" Willie applauded and shuffled through a rack of veils. "This will complete the look." She knotted my hair up into a makeshift bun and held a handful of tulle over my head.

I scrunched up my face. Despite the flattering flow of the fabric, something wasn't quite right. I looked stiff, an uptight version of myself. Un-huggable. Turning again and studying my form from every angle, the realization hit me like a handful of rice. The shapely sleek woman in the mirror was a beautiful bride, but she wasn't me.

"Hold on a minute." I left Kati and Willie talking excitedly about hair accessories and satin heels and returned to the dressing room.

In the privacy of the room, I ran my hand down over my foundation flat tummy, feeling the tiny pearls woven into the design on the skirt and couldn't help remembering another dress from another time. When I was young, I had a dream wedding straight out of a fairytale. For months, my mother and I planned every detail from the *stefana* (floral crowns my husband and I would wear as we walked around the altar) to the Greek party favors (tiny bundles of sugar-coated almonds wrapped in net and tied with a satin bow for every guest).

She made sure her oldest daughter was impeccable from the breathtaking veil on her head to the pearl covered gown to the tip of her cathedral length train.

Now that I was older and summoning up the courage to tie the knot again, I knew that a perfect figure, or a perfect wedding, didn't guarantee a perfect marriage.

I unzipped the gown and watched it slip to the floor. The uncomfortable pair of Spanx followed. I took a deep breath, now that I could, and felt my body relax back into its natural shape. I reached for the last dress, one that had been hidden behind all the other gowns, overshadowed by the brighter, more dramatic ones. I stepped into it, pulled it effortlessly over my hips and zipped it up. Then I went out to model the gown, dreading how it would fit without commercial grade reinforcement. Lifting the lacy skirt, I stepped up onto the pedestal and stood in front of the mirror one last time, vulnerable, but willing to accept myself, lumps, and all.

Staring back at me was a middle age woman in a lovely dress that hugged her like an old friend, and bathed her soft figure in shimmering shades of champagne. Simple and strapless, it seemed to understand her, forgive her, as it shimmied along her shape, delicate designs of antique lace dripping down the length of her strong but imperfect body. Every scar of her life glistened under the bright lights, every wrinkle twinkled, every pound was unbound, but finally she felt free to live and love without anything to hold her in, or hold her back. She wasn't twenty, or thirty, or even forty, and didn't want to be. The bride was vintage, like her gown.

Her eyes, lined lightly from a lifetime of laughter flashed playfully at the reflection in the mirror. She was young at heart and it showed. But the most beautiful thing about her was that she was smiling.

"Yes!" Willie smiled and nodded in approval. She wiped her eyes with a monogrammed handkerchief. "It's just like the one I wore for my fourth wedding."

I laughed, looked over at my daughter and pretended to hold a bouquet. "Here Comes the Bride, *not* dressed in white."

"I love it! It's so you, Mom." Kati snapped a photo of me with her phone, then moved closer to get a selfie of the two of us, mother and daughter hugging, each flashing her diamond engagement ring for the camera.

"I'm next!" Kati grabbed my arm. "Willie made me an appointment for next week. I can't wait to find the perfect dress!"

"I can't wait either, baby."

Picturing the perfect wedding I would plan for my daughter, my eyes filled with tears. I imagined her just six months from now in a gorgeous white beaded gown and a flowing veil, following my footsteps, walking down the same aisle, in the same church, to stand before the same altar— the one my mother had stood before fifty years ago. Despite everything, I still believed in happily ever after. And that was the butter-cream icing on the wedding cake.

In the end, I said no thanks to the Spanx. I wanted none of the bun. I yelled no way in *hell* to the veil.

I said yes to this dress.

The Toast

I tapped a silver spoon against a crystal flute of champagne cupped in my fingers. The delicate dinging sound danced across the ballroom. As mother of the bride, it was my job to welcome the guests who had just been served Greek salads piled high with feta cheese and topped with a tangy lemon vinaigrette. Posed in front of the head table, note cards in hand, I gazed out at the crowd through a pair of false eyelashes that had started to slip and smiled as I said, "I'd like to make a toast."

Actually, I'd like to *get* totally toasted. That would be later when I could collapse in a corner with my friends and down a couple rounds of Blushing Brides, the fruity, vodka drenched signature drink my daughter, Kati, chose for her big, fat, Greek wedding reception. Just a simple five-minute speech and I could peel off my fake eyelashes, kick off these hellacious heels, let down my hair and all my cares, and Greek dance circles around my ex-husband and his extended family.

"I want to thank everyone for being here to celebrate this special occasion." I glanced at my new husband who I'd married six months before. "This is our family's second wedding this year," I paused while the crowd commiserated with good-natured chuckles and groans. "I had the unbelievable experience of being engaged at the same time as my daughter, and I learned one thing—if you can survive the planning of a wedding, the marriage should be a piece of cake—white chocolate raspberry, in this case."

I shook my head recalling my own engagement just the year before, when Cowboy surprised me with a proposal production. He dropped down on one knee in front of all my family and friends as the flash mob he'd hired danced to *Marry Me* in front of a fountain in Uptown Park. Luckily, I didn't surprise *him* by saying no.

Kati, who was just developing her photography business, had the inside scoop on wedding dresses, venues and modern-day etiquette. She swooped in to help me plan everything, even doubling as a bridesmaid and wedding photographer/coordinator on the big day. I had barely gotten used to seeing a diamond ring sparkling on my own left hand again when my younger daughter, Kristina, began obsessing about her older sister's marital status.

"I wonder when Kati and Alex will get married?" Kristina always started these conversations when we were alone in the car so I'd be forced to answer.

"Not for a long time!" I turned up the radio to avoid the discussion. "They're still in college. They're way too young!"

Kristina rolled her eyes and looked out the window, a slow smirk spreading across her face. The topic would come up again and again in one form or another for the next few months as my two daughters teamed up, grooming me to get used to a groom.

I looked down at my crumpled notes. "Kati and Alex were high school sweethearts. This is no easy accomplishment when you have a Greek mother who won't let you date." My dad winked at me while our Greek guests laughed good-naturedly and the non-Greeks looked at each other, puzzled.

I remembered having mixed feelings when Kati came home one day from school her junior year with a seemingly innocent announcement. "There's some random boy who keeps wanting to play Words with Friends with me." She curled her lip and shook her head but peeked at me from under her lashes to gauge my reaction. *Just ignore him. Don't talk to strangers! Do I know his family?* My motherly instincts had always smothered any romantic sparks before they could catch fire. But this time, maybe because I was burning with a romance of my own, I surprised us both. "It's just a silly word game." I tossed my head and scoffed. "What could possibly come of that?"

I glanced at the bride and groom. "*This* is what came of it!"

The happy couple looked into each other's eyes and smiled like they were the only ones in the room. I wanted to tell Alex that although he may have won a few rounds of Words with Friends with his high school sweetheart, in the real-life game of Words with Wife, Kati would always have the last one. Alex was clever enough to ease his way into our home. He discovered early on that the way to this family's heart was through our stomachs and he made sure we were never hungry. He discovered if he came through the door carrying carbs this protective Greek mother would melt into a sugar coma at his feet.

At the first Thanksgiving we celebrated together, he showed up with apple and cherry pies he had baked himself. After learning we loved spicy chicken rigatoni from Bucca de Beppos, this future engineer fed his fascination of how things are put together by figuring out how to duplicate their recipe. Volunteering to cook dinner for us was a great excuse for him to see Kati and as a result, we enjoyed spicy chicken rigatoni at least once a week for years.

Calm, serious, left-brain Alex balanced out our crazy, creative, right-brain family. Fearless, he witnessed more family meltdowns than I care to admit. Relaxed and patient, he was always there to quietly save the day. In our own way, we were grooming him for Kati.

I cocked one eyebrow and caught my ex-husband's eye across the room as I continued my toast, "Marriage has its ups and downs." I grinned as he squirmed in his seat. "This happy couple's honeymoon will never end, but there are sure to be trials that will only make them stronger." I dropped my voice to a stage whisper and confessed to the roomful of guests, "Despite her impeccable upbringing, Kati is not perfect."

Turning to my new son-in-law, I shook my head. "Alex, don't say I didn't warn you when you walk into her closet for the first time and got swallowed up by a sea of sweaters and sneakers and slippers and shirts. You thought you witnessed the aftermath of a tornado, or an H&M dressing room five minutes before closing time. But you're just learning what happens to Kati's good fashion sense when she's running fashionably late. And just wait until Kati spots that first bug in the new love nest you share. Your reasonable, smart, beautiful bride will morph into a weeping, wailing fishmonger's wife. She'll jump up onto the nearest chair and refuse to come down until it's dead. If you're not there to slay the winged dragon, she'll wait on that chair until you race home, search under every piece of furniture and kill the bitty beast, which after suffering through hours of Kati's screeching, will welcome a swift death by shoe. Don't think you can trick her, either, by stomping around blindly in the next room. Kati will insist on seeing the carcass. Let's hope you don't come home hungry, unless you're prepared to cook. Although your new wife has too many skills to mention, whipping up a gourmet meal is not one of them. If you think you can survive off of love and the occasional sandwich, think again. Kati has an unfounded phobia of lunchmeat. She'd rather starve than touch a slippery, slimy, paper-thin slice of turkey with her bare hands. When her siblings wanted to torture her, all they had to do was peel off a piece from a package of Buddigs and threaten to rub it on her face. So, marriage to Kati means martyring yourself to a lifetime of lunch making. If you have two children—which we're all eagerly awaiting—in the twelve years they will attend school, you will make almost five thousand sandwiches for their lunch boxes, not counting weekends, holidays or summer vacation!"

I studied Alex sitting at the head table, bowtie shaking slightly as he swallowed. "But the amazing ups of marriage will make you forget the downs. Kati has a good eye—after all, she picked you. As a photographer, she focuses on the good and finds beauty in the ordinary. She brings out the best in people. She sets goals and exceeds them. She is strong and responsible, loving and kind. She gives great advice. My advice to you is to take it. Although neither of you may be perfect, you two are a perfect match, and I know your life together will be happy and blessed. You bring out the best in each other. As long as you put God first in your hearts, your marriage will be strong. A cord of three strands is not easily broken."

I folded my notes and looked at my daughter's new husband. "Alex, I'm proud to call you my son-in-law. You're not just marrying Kati. You're marrying into our big, fat Greek family. We'll always be here for you two." I cocked one eyebrow. "Whether you like it or not."

With a festive flourish, I raised my glass of champagne. The crystal caught the twinkling of the candles on the table and cast prisms of light and love onto the newlyweds by my side. "Everyone please join me in wishing our favorite couple a life of love, laughter and happily ever after." I smiled as the guests clapped and tapped their glasses together.

The young woman I mothered and nurtured for twenty-two years, glowing like a princess in a white lace gown, turned and kissed her new husband on the lips. In that moment I realized that she was no longer mine. We would no longer share a home or a last name— it wouldn't be the same. I took a tiny sip of champagne. The icy bubbles tickled the lump in my throat and caused my eyes to water.

The rest of the evening whirled by like a wedding waltz. The band played, the guests danced, bartenders poured drinks from an open bar. As mother of the bride, I circulated the room, mingling and mixing until I was mentally spent. When I finally found a moment to sit down and kick off my shoes, I breathed a sigh of relief.

My eyes settled on a party favor one of the guests had left on the table. I picked up the *boubouniera* and cradled the tiny bundle of candy-coated almonds in my hand. Greek tradition has it that the combination of the sugary shell and the nutty almond within symbolizes the bittersweet nature of marriage. An odd number of nuts are used because they cannot be divided in two, just as the newly married couple are now one and cannot be separated. I'd made hundreds of these with my mother for my first and second weddings, and now my daughter's. *If only marriage were as simple as this.*

I was slipping the favor into my purse when Alex walked up grinning. His bowtie was loosened and he held a small dessert plate in each hand. I smiled up at him. "What's that?"

"Pie!" He sat down beside me and placed a plate in front of each of us. "I thought you could use a piece."

Kati had opted to trade the traditional groom's cake for a tower of groom's pies instead, and Alex was eating it up. I picked up a fork and stabbed the flaky crust, speared a dark red piece of fruit, and popped it into my mouth. Closing my eyes, I savored the flavors—the perfect dash of sweetness married with a pinch of tart—swirling on my tongue. "*Mmm.* Delicious."

He was halfway through his piece of apple when he turned to me, dark eyes twinkling. "I think I can make this at home." He nodded as if calculating the recipe in his mind. "Green apples for sure..." He licked a crumb from his bottom lip. "Dark brown sugar. I bet they use cold butter for the crust. I can't wait to surprise Kati and everyone at Thanksgiving!"

It must have been the sugar rush that made me feel so warm inside. I smiled at my new son-in-law and nodded my head.

For some couples, marriage is not a piece of cake. But for these lucky two, it would be easy as pie.

Hair of the Dog

Shortly after my son, Alston, graduated from college and moved to Dallas for his new job, he felt lonely and got a dog. With my son five hours from Houston and my two daughters away at college, I was lonely, too. I got a new husband.

We both felt better.

Sinbad, a Siberian Husky, gave Alston a new leash on life. Suddenly there was someone waiting for him when he got back to his apartment every evening after work. Training his new dog proved to be a challenge that took up most of his once lonely hours. Suddenly, my son was needed and loved and that made both of us happy. Ironically Cowboy had much of the same effect on me.

Cowboy required little training. He repaired everything that was broken in my empty nest, including my heart. A cross between the Marlboro man and Martha Stewart, he cooked and cleaned and brought life back into my home; still, all the spackle in the world couldn't fill the holes left in a house where children used to live. I missed my children and being a hands-on mom.

When my son announced he was coming to visit the following weekend and bringing his new pet, my heart swelled with anticipation. I stocked up on chewy treats and specialty bones, bought rubber balls and rings, and a fluffy pet bed that I topped off with a squeaky teddy bear. I imagined cozy nights sitting by the fire, Sinbad curled asleep by my feet, or taking him for long walks in the park, our footsteps crunching over the fallen leaves. I wasn't sure who I was more excited to see, my son or my new grand-dog.

My husband eyed the orthopedic fleece dog bed in the kitchen and shook his head. "It's not sleeping in the house, is it?" Where he came from dogs herded, hunted or retrieved and slept outside. He looked at the floor he'd just mopped. "Boy I hope it doesn't shed."

I ignored him and planned a small surprise party, inviting friends and family over to welcome the pair. Kati and Kristina drove home from their colleges and my parents came over to meet the new member of the family. The table was laid out with all of Alston's favorite foods, the centerpiece: a chocolate cake with *Welcome Sinbad* written in white frosting. We sat in the living room eagerly awaiting their arrival.

We heard the hum of the garage door opening and jumped up from our chairs in front of the television, leaving Cowboy alone watching *Snow Dogs*. I grabbed the plate of chocolate chip cookies I'd just baked to celebrate and stood by the door.

"Sit! Sinbad, sit!" Alston's voice echoed in the garage. We heard crashing and banging then the garage door closing. "Come back here! Sit!"

The kitchen door cracked open and we waited expectantly. Then a whirlwind of white fur burst through the door pulling my son on a leash behind it, knocking the plate of cookies out of my hand and onto the floor. My grand-dog lunged at me, jumping up to lick my face, almost toppling me over as well. Then he lost interest, attacked a cookie and ran down the hall, Alston following close behind.

"Sur-prise!?" the half-hearted exclamation escaped from my lips.

"No Sinbad!" Alston leaped through the air and landed on his pet, wrestling another cookie from its jaws.

"Chocolate is bad for dogs! Mom, what were you thinking?"

"But they're your favorites." I could see Cowboy scowling from his place on the couch. "I made sweet potato chews for Sinbad."

"Must be the reason 'bad' is in its name," Cowboy muttered from the couch.

Alston tightened his grip on the leash, took a deep breath and leaned down to hug me. His arms felt more muscular, his face fuller than I remembered. He seemed to have become a man overnight. I planted a kiss on his forehead inhaling the irresistible smell of boy and dog. I relished the joyful feeling of having everyone I loved under one roof, at least for one evening.

I bent down to pet Sinbad on the head, admiring his beautiful winter coat and sapphire eyes. He allowed two pats before he jumped to his feet and shook his body violently, as if trying to shrug off his fur coat as well as my affection, a poof of white fluff forming a cloud over the kitchen. Then he broke free from Alston and ran unrestrained, dodging our guests' legs in his rush to explore.

Cowboy lumbered up from the couch and stretched to his full height. His jaw tightened as his gaze fell over the kitchen, now dusted with a fine layer of glistening white, like new fallen snow. His immaculate house had gone to the dogs and the determined glint in his eye declared he was taking it back.

I saw my dad eying a pot of chili simmering on the stove. Relieved for an excuse to ease the tension, I called everyone into the kitchen with a, "Let's eat!"

"Sure smells good," my dad said spooning out a hearty portion of his son-in-law's cowboy chili. He looked down at the steaming bowl and frowned. "When did you start putting Parmesan on the chili?"

Cowboy looked at me in alarm. Before we could stop him, my dad took a huge bite and nodded at Cowboy. "Best damn chili you've ever made." Thin strands of white clung to his lips like a moustache. "The cheese really makes it."

Cowboy peered into the chili pot. "That's not Parmesan," he hissed so only I could hear.

"And coconut cake!" my mom exclaimed cutting into the dessert.

"Coconut?" I rushed over to the table and peered over my mother's shoulder. My chocolate welcome home cake was sprinkled with flecks of white. I stuck my finger into the frosting, licked it and gagged. *That's not coconut.* I snatched the cake off the table and glared at Sinbad who had tired of running circles around the house and was making himself at home on my leather sofa, happily watching *Snow Dogs* and chewing on the remote like it was a bone.

"He's sitting in my place." Cowboy's face reddened. "Someone needs to train that dog. If you're not going to do something, I will."

He started towards the family room and I caught his arm. "But he just got here. Let him play."

Cowboy ignored me and marched up to Sinbad. The two stared at each other, not blinking, Alpha man to Alpha dog. I held my breath. Then Sinbad let out a husky bark, leaped off the couch and raced out of the room, leaving Cowboy shaking his head and wiping dog fur off his favorite spot in front of the television. He picked up the mangled remote and pounded on the buttons, but the channel was now permanently set to the Sinbad's favorite station.

The girls helped me skim the dog hair off the chili and scrape the coconut-colored fur (and most of the frosting) from the cake. Guests milled around the kitchen and family room helping themselves to food that could be rinsed off before consuming.

"Carrots, anyone? Celery?" I passed a veggie tray around and refilled everyone's drinks with something stronger. A little hair of the dog would get this party started. Soon Alston was entertaining everyone with stories about his new job and the joys of being a dog owner. I inhaled deeply and exhaled, encouraging the tension to leave my body. Everything was under control. No reason to get excited about a little dog hair.

Except that it was too quiet. My mom antenna sprang to attention, the tiny hairs on the back of my neck prickled and posed, waiting for action. I planned a quick round of the house, certain I would find nothing more than Sinbad napping in a cozy corner.

Wandering nonchalantly through the family room, I smiled and nodded. Cowboy looked up at me with suspicion, but the others chuckled along with the canine movie stuck on the screen. The kitchen was a normal mess of dirty pots and pans, half-filled drinks and abandoned plates of food. I crept up the stairs and peeked into the darkened bedrooms. **Silence.** It wasn't until I spotted the master bedroom, its door halfway ajar, that my maternal radar went into high alert. My heart pounded as I approached the door and almost stopped when I came face to muzzle with Sinbad.

He was standing on my bed, one hind leg hovering over Cowboy's favorite down pillow. Before I could stop him, he left his mark, gazing at me with the defiance of a teenager, daring me to challenge him.

"Sinbad!" I commanded, "get off the bed!"

He looked away and yawned, then curled up at the foot of the bed.

"I mean it."

He jumped up, then crouched his head down, his tail in the air, staring at me, ready to pounce. I moved toward him and he bounded off the bed, ran into the bathroom where he tipped over our laundry basket, strewing dirty socks and shirts across the floor.

"Sinbad, sit!" I cried, and miraculously, he did. I tiptoed towards him. He was growling softly and gnawing on a scrap of something black like it was steak and he hadn't eaten in days. He looked up and smirked. It was then I saw it. Hanging out of the corner of his mouth was a pair of my sheerest, most expensive, honeymoon quality, panties.

"Oh no you don't!" I growled in my most threatening Cujo voice.

He bit into the panties, closed his eyes and shook his head savagely, thrashing them from left to right. I leaped to grab them from his mouth, caught the edge of the lace and pulled with all my might. Thinking it was a game, Sinbad bit down even harder, playing tug-of-war with me, then he wrenched his head and pulled the fabric free from my hand, causing me to lose my balance and sprawl to the floor.

"Give the panties to Mommy," I pleaded on all fours.

He cocked his head and grinned, eyes twinkling. I'd seen that look before. It was the one Cowboy wore at the altar on our wedding day. *I love you and I'll be your companion forever*, it said, *but you'll never tame me.*

He bowed his head for a moment, a half-apology for what he was about to do, then he jumped over me and sprang out of the bedroom and down the stairs, sporting the panties proudly in his mouth like a trophy. I chased after him, breathing hard, as he raced through the kitchen, past my parents and the guests, shamelessly parading Victoria's secret through the party.

My heart leaped when the panties briefly caught on a doorknob. Sinbad slowed for a second, then feeling the resistance, ran at full speed, pulling like only a Husky can do, stretching the undergarment to unmentionable proportions, almost spanning the length of the house. *They never stretch like that when I'm wearing the uncomfortable things!* I marveled at the size of them. The house could wear my panties to a block party. Alaska could fit inside my panties, giving new meaning to one size fits all.

I dove for the incriminating intimates and just when I thought I had them, the lace slipped off the knob, snapping Sinbad on the back of the neck like the tip of a whip. I missed and he mushed, with me in hot pursuit. I chased him into the family room where he paused under the coffee table only long enough to check out the ending of *Snow Dogs*.

"Cowboy, grab him!" I pointed to the coffee table. "He's under there!"

"Under where?" He looked down at Sinbad, and corrected himself. "I mean, under *wear*."

"Sinbad got into a little something upstairs," I said to the roomful of guests.

"Too bad he didn't get into a little Nair," grumbled Cowboy.

"What's that in his mouth?" my dad demanded. "There's a piece of string caught in his teeth." He whistled. "Here, Sinbad!"

Humiliated, I looked up to the heavens. *If only it were Cowboy's briefs, an innocent pair of granny panties, a sporty stretch of Spanx, anything but my...*

"I didn't see a thong. I mean a thing." Cowboy's eyes met mine across the room and his voice dripped with sarcasm, "But he just got here. Let him play."

Just then Alston walked into the room. Sinbad looked up at him, panting. "What's that in your mouth, Buddy?" Alston crouched down to get a closer look. "Isn't anyone keeping an eye on him? He could choke."

Swallow it, I begged. *I'll pay for a trip to the emergency vet.*

Alston's hand was inches from Sinbad's mouth and a lifetime of therapy when Kristina shouted from the kitchen. "Sinbad!" She shook the container of sweet potato chews, enticing him with the sound while she waved a treat in the air. "Come and get it! It's the only food in the house not covered with dog hair."

I shot her a look of appreciation.

"Ironic, isn't it?" she said.

Sinbad bounded towards her, stopped abruptly at her feet and allowed her to pet him and trade his silky treat for a chewy one. "What's that in your mouth?" she spoke loudly for everyone to hear. "Did you get into Kati's suitcase?" Kristina plucked up what was left of the panties with two fingers and tossed them in the trashcan. She covered her mouth and whispered so only I could hear, "You owe me Mom."

I walked back into the living room to survey the damage. The last of the guests were brushing themselves off and saying their goodbyes as the credits to *Snow Dog* scrolled up the screen. Alston was promising my parents he'd come back to visit real soon, maybe next time with a girlfriend. But the sweetest sight of all was Cowboy snoring softly on the sofa with Sinbad curled up in a snowy white ball at his feet. They look so innocent when they're asleep.

"We had a wonderful time," my mom said hugging me.

My dad slipped cash into each of the grandchildren's hands and stooped down to pet Sinbad. "I like your dog. He's got spirit." He grabbed a sweet potato treat off the counter. "What's this, a cookie?" Before we could stop him, he took a huge bite. "Not bad." He worked his jaw and grimaced. "A little chewy, but better than that coconut cake you were serving."

The next morning, my eyes filled with tears as I stood at the driveway and said goodbye to my children one-by-one. Kati took off for A&M in a red Mustang, her long, curly hair blowing in the wind. Kristina departed for Lubbock in a white Honda, classic rock blaring with a pair my favorite boots and the promise of a new iPhone. I figured I got off easy. Alston backed out of the driveway last, a Chevy Tahoe packed with Sinbad's supplies and toys and a week's worth of homemade cookies. Cowboy came outside to see the pair off and raised his hand in a half wave. When Sinbad saw him, he stuck his head out the rear window, his tongue hanging in a happy grin. White fuzz blew off his head like dandelion seeds and floated in the breeze towards us.

Alston honked, Sinbad howled, and Cowboy planted his hands on his hips and shook his head. I waved goodbye until the back of the truck disappeared from sight. Then I wiped my eyes and smiled.

After all, I hadn't lost a son. I'd gained a dog.

Plumb Crazy

My husband is a handyman. I met him ten years ago during a vulnerable time of life when I was nearing middle age, and so was my house, and we were both in desperate need of repair. I had a honey-do list a mile long and the HOA breathing down my back when some friends at church set us up on a blind date. I showed up in a little black dress and a nervous smile. He rolled up with a magical Mid-western tool belt and a roll of duct tape, equipped to fix anything and everything.

It wasn't long before he spackled and painted his way into my heart. I discovered there was nothing he couldn't fix. Rotting baseboards from two Houston hurricanes ago? **No problem.** Bulbs burnt out twenty feet up since before my oldest child was born in 1992? **No big deal.** My ex's favorite color glaring at me from the master bedroom walls? **All in a day's work.** Broken windows, broken locks, broken hearts? **"I can fix that,"** he drawled. He had the strength and skill of ten contractors all rolled up into one burly package. He tackled every job on my list with Nebraska know-how and a smile, then had the energy to take me out for dinner and dancing afterwards.

He never complained like other men I knew. I once witnessed him drill a bit through his thumb. I screamed and almost fainted as blood spurted out all over the kitchen floor, and frantically searched for my cell phone to call 911. Not even a cuss word escaped his lips. He calmly whipped out a worn handkerchief from his back pocket, wrapped up his wound and finished the job, using his other nine fingers.

So when I left the house one Saturday morning to attend a writing workshop, I felt confident leaving him alone with one simple honey-do assignment. "It sure would be nice if *we* could paint the bathroom upstairs before the kids come to visit." I emphasized 'we' so he would feel this fun project would be a joint effort, even though we both knew there was nothing handy about my hands. My son was bringing his new girlfriend home for the first time and I wanted the house to be perfect. "Maybe a shade like Kilim Beige," I continued, as if the hue had just popped into my mind on the way out the door and wasn't something I'd agonized over for weeks with my mother, my aunt and a Sherwin Williams color consultant.

"We'll see," he said from the couch. We both knew this meant he would jump through hoops to get it done before I got home so I could marvel at his skill and talent. We also both knew this job was so simple he could do it with one paintbrush tied behind his back.

It was hard for me to focus on the workshop that day. Instead of finding my writing voice, I fantasized about the fresh new bathroom that would welcome me when I got home. Instead of fighting writer's block, I daydreamed about going to Target and selecting fluffy new towels and rugs for the renovated room. I imagined my son's look of delight when he saw the soothing spa color. I could barely wait for the workshop to end so I could rush home. If I hurried, I might make it to Home Depot before they closed to buy a new light fixture for above the sink.

I smiled as I turned onto my street. *There's nothing sexier than a man who can fix things.* I felt sorry for those poor women married to handy-challenged doctors or lawyers. What did they do when the A/C broke down on a hot August afternoon? Take two aspirins and argue about who was going to fix it?

I pulled up to the house and gathered my purchases from the trunk. Barely able to see over the bags in my arms, I kicked at the back door. "Honey, I'm home." When Cowboy didn't show up to unlock the door and greet me with open arms, I gave up and fumbled for my key. "Wait 'til you see the new things I got for the bathroom." The sweetheart was probably taking a nap while the paint dried. I put down my things and looked for him at his favorite spot on the couch. It was then I heard it. A growling sound like that of a trapped animal echoed from upstairs. I froze. "Cowboy?"

Banging and clanging erupted from above. A slew of un-Cowboy like words assaulted my ears. "Mother flushing piece of..."

I bounded up the stairs two at a time and raced into my son's bathroom. An arsenal of wrenches and pliers and screwdrivers littered the floor. The toilet was pulled from its spot on the tile and a gaping hole yawned where it used to sit. The faucet was yanked from the sink and the marble countertop was smeared with grease and chipped in two places. A single light bulb flickered from a dangling wire. The bathroom hadn't looked this bad since my son lived at home.

"Cowboy!" I yelled over the ruckus and ran over to the pair of blue jeaned legs sprawled out from beneath the bathroom cabinet. "What's going on here?"

My husband's lower body protruded from under the sink, his linebacker chest jammed into the right side of a 24-inch cabinet. "Can't. Loosen. This..." he planted his work boots on the tile floor, his legs quivering from the strain, "freaking..." a sharp sound came from the cabinet when his elbow slammed against the floor, "pipe!" A torrent of water and curse words flooded out from the dark bowels of the cabinet.

I grabbed for some bath towels to stop the flow and considered sticking one in his potty mouth as well. "Come out so we can clean up this mess." I planted hands on my hips to survey the disaster, eyes settling on my husband's bare tummy that protruded over his tool belt where his t-shirt had risen up. Clearly the handymoon was over.

An unopened can of Kilim Beige taunted me from a corner on the floor. I tapped my foot, calculating how long it would take to repair the damage. Plumbers weren't cheap, or electricians. If we didn't start on this soon, my son and his girlfriend would be staying at the Holiday Inn, and I might join them there, indefinitely. I waved a hand at the mess and asked the inevitable, "Why, Cowboy?"

"I came in here to paint and heard the toilet running. I figured that would be a quick fix." I raised my eyebrows. "Then I saw one of the handles on the sink was leaking. When I went to tighten it, the whole thing snapped off. Cheap builder brands!" He banged on the pipes some more then grew still.

All I wanted was for the walls to be painted. I ran a hand through my hair. I could Kilim. "Did you fall asleep down there?" I felt him rolling his eyes at me. Then he dropped the F bomb.

"That's not necessary and very disrespectful," I lectured my husband. My marriage might be going down the drain but my self-esteem wasn't going with it.

"I said, I'm STUCK," Cowboy growled while fighting to twist his torso free.

I got down on my hands and knees and crawled up to him to investigate. Sure enough, somehow his shoulders, chest and arms had cleared the small opening on the right side of the cabinet, but the solid strip of wood that divided it in half imprisoned him. His green eyes glowered at me from the dark cabinet cave.

"Just breathe. Now push." I pulled on his legs and the vanity moaned like it was giving birth to an overgrown breech baby, but Cowboy didn't budge. "Just our luck," I mumbled under my breath.

"Now who's disrespectful?"

"I said you really are STUCK." I stood up and made a decision. "I'm calling the fire department."

He kicked and screamed while I hurried to find my phone, tripping on his discarded tools on my way out of the bathroom. I spotted a handsaw on the floor and paused. *How hard could it be?* I picked it up and lightly touched the blade. Empowered, I headed back toward to the bathroom with a gleam in my eye. He might not be the sharpest tool in the shed, but he was my husband and I was going to save him. Besides, he wasn't getting out of painting the bathroom that easily. I returned to the bathroom and crouched down next to his body, brandishing the blade inches from his family tools.

He looked at me in horror. "Put the saw down."

I ignored him and ran the blade across the divider, relishing the sound of the metal tearing into the wood.

"You don't, know what, you're doing." He spoke slowly with a forced calmness, as if he were addressing a crazed axe murderer. "Put down the Craftsman."

I continued to saw, gleaning great satisfaction watching dust fly from the frame. Then my hand slipped and the saw sliced through the air and landed blade down on his crotch.

"Are you trying to kill me? Go! Just go." Cowboy kicked a size 11 work boot in my direction.

"Fine. Get yourself out." I stormed down the stairs and straight into the kitchen. I was starving and food might help me concentrate. I turned on the burner, poured olive oil into a pan and added onion. I was still fuming as I wiped splatters of oil off the countertop, feeling the slick liquid on my fingertips. *Olive oil!* I grabbed the extra virgin and raced up the stairs.

Cowboy grunted when I returned to his side, waving the bottle. His eyes widened as I unscrewed the top and drizzled the fragrant liquid all over his exposed torso, like I was preparing a turkey to be roasted. His legs stopped kicking as I rubbed the oil into his skin.

"Do you really think this is the time and place?" he said. "I'm not into this type of thing."

"I'll be gentle," I said as I greased the wood divider, allowing the oil to coat the bottom of the cabinet. "If you squeezed in, you can squeeze out." I grabbed one of his arms trying to pull him on his side. "Work with me here."

Cowboy took an enormous breath, sucked in his stomach and slithered out of the cabinet and onto the bathroom floor. Exhausted from the effort, we lay side-by-side, breathing hard and staring at the ceiling, laughing.

Cowboy sighed. "*Mmmm,*" he said. "Something smells good."

I took a deep sniff. "It does. Like my grandmother's kitchen growing up." I tried to place the aroma. Freshly chopped onions sautéed in... "Oh, no!"

I gasped as smoke filled the air and detectors screeched off in unison. We almost didn't hear the sirens-- or the banging on the door.

Cowboy jumped up and looked out the window. "I told you not to call the fire department! I got out, didn't I?"

"I didn't call them!" I cried over my shoulder as I flew down the stairs. It turned out that a tiny little grease fire had set off the alarm. Accidents happen and the firemen were very understanding, though they looked at Cowboy's oil slicked upper body with suspicion and shook their heads as they walked out the door. The kitchen was a mess, soot marks stained the walls and a fine residue of pale, yellow powder coated the countertops and most of the floor. Now two rooms of the house were a disaster.

I looked up at Cowboy and grinned. "I promise to never cook again." He snorted. I squinted at the walls. "Have you noticed how badly the kitchen needs to be painted?" I swiped a fingertip over the yellowy powder by the sink and examined the shade under the light. "Something cheerful, maybe? A nice, warm buttery hue... I'll have to ask my mom."

He surveyed the room with a critical eye and shook his head when his gaze landed on the kitchen sink. "We're not painting anything until I fix that leaky faucet."

"Oh no!" I threw up my hands. "Never mind. It can wait." Marriage requires maintenance, and so does a house. Over the years I've learned some things are easier to fix than others.

But if he thinks I'm letting him anywhere near my pipes again ... he's plumb crazy.

Wall-to-Wall

The tan-skinned counselor eyed us expectantly, her delicate hands holding a pad and pen. My husband and I settled down as far apart as possible from each other on a beige colored loveseat across from her. The small room was painted a soft shade of neutral, which matched the expression on her face.

Struggling to appear sane, I held a plush pillow on my lap and tried on different expressions for the pleasant looking woman as if I were in a dressing room at Nordstrom's, seeing what fit me best in front of the mirror. I began with a toothy, eager smile, but worried it sent a manic message. A more serious face marked me as depressed. I willed myself to stop picking at the nubs on the pillow, not wanting to appear anxious, finally settling on a soft smile. I glanced at my husband from the corner of my eye.

His battle-worn face was weathered and grim, his jaw line strong and unyielding. Both boots were planted on the invisible line he'd painted on the floor. The one I'd crossed. *I'm not crazy*, his body language shouted, *my wife is!*

"So, what brings you here today?" the counselor's voice had a soothing lilt to it, a gentle accent I couldn't place. She seemed immune to our stress and sung her words like a lullaby.

I extended an open palm to my husband, a courtesy I didn't feel. "Why don't *you* tell her?"

Silent fury seethed from his pores and his right eye twitched.

"I can feel you're in a lot of pain." The counselor studied us and waited with the patience of a saint. "I'm here to help." She leaned closer.

I stared down at the faded Oriental rug beneath my feet and the traumatic events of the weekend welled up in my memory. I shook my head and met her gaze. "Carpet." My shoulders slumped from the weight of my confession. "We got new carpet."

"When my family first moved into our new home in Green Trails" ... I explained the issue in rushed words and a warbling voice ... "we took off our shoes at the backdoor and left them all in a row. No food was allowed upstairs, or drinks, but as time went by, and the newness faded, the rules weakened. No drinks turned into clear drinks, then anything but red wine. No food turned into dry popcorn, then anything but spaghetti and meat sauce. Soon the speckled cream frieze read like a worn roadmap of my family's footprints."

The neutral face nodded for me to continue.

"There's a sticky greenish glob of goo upstairs," I admitted, taking her on a virtual tour of our home. "Science experiment, 2003."

She raised her eyebrows.

"Next to it is an inky blob of blue," I continued as we walked down memory lane. "A leaky ballpoint pen didn't make the grade. Finals week, 2005."

She murmured for me to go on.

I shrugged in resignation. "A teensy bit of gold glitter dots the floor where my youngest made a poster for eagle mascot tryouts." I smiled brightly. "She won, by the way!"

The counselor awarded me with a soft smile.

"And that blob of red that looks like blood?" I wrinkled my nose. "It's just a smear of fire engine red lipstick. The girls playing dress-up, you know."

The truth was that I'd grown sentimental about the stains, my map of motherhood. The disgusting brown blotch by the TV was just chocolate milk my oldest spilled while playing video games. It was inches away from a matching-colored plop of puppy poop, Sinbad 2015.

I longed to waltz over wheat-colored wall-to-wall, but it made no sense to get new carpet while my three rug rats were still underfoot. When one-by-one they went off to college, I had little reason to go upstairs, and it was easy to forget the matted mess. Then when my daughter got engaged, a new Berber wasn't in the budget.

Things changed when I remarried.

"How did things change?" my counselor wanted to know.

"My husband was disgusted by the carpet. He asked about a moldy patch on the floor." I leaned closer to the counselor, lowering my voice. "Harvey. Roof leak, 2017."

She nodded as if she understood.

"And he came to the brilliant deduction that we needed new carpet." I paused with my story, lost in thought.

The counselor's eyes lit up and she leaned forward. "So you came together to try to solve the problem?"

My husband snorted.

I glared at him. "The real problem wasn't the carpet." I looked off into the distance. "It was the closets."

I'd preserved my children's former bedrooms upstairs with the precision of a museum curator, allowing their artifacts to form shrines only a mother could love. Trophies from every sport lined my 26-year-old son's room, his first stuffed animal, a well-loved Simba, peeked out from under his bed. The girls' rooms were lovingly littered with pom-poms and yearbooks, concert tickets and discarded clothes from the 90s. It was no surprise I hadn't addressed the carpet issue. I couldn't *see* the carpet.

I knew I couldn't get new carpet until their closet floors were picked up and tidy. For years, I begged my grown children, "Please come home and clean out your rooms." When that didn't work, I tried bribing them with food, "I'll make lasagna. It'll be fun." I resorted to bartering, "I'll watch your dog over the weekend if you promise to go through your things." Then I threatened, "No clean rooms, no Christmas. Ever."

But when Christmas came, I'd buy them more clothes and gadgets, some they would pack in their suitcases and take to their own homes, some I'd find months later stuffed into their childhood closets.

Tired of my complaining at every family holiday, they finally teamed up and planned an intervention. "Mom, just give it all away!" I couldn't. I wouldn't. Each homecoming mum, each prom photo, each straight A report card was a milestone in my life, as well as theirs.

After I finally chose new carpet, put down a deposit and scheduled the installation date with A1 Floors 4U, I still put off the inevitable.

I approached my husband who was sprawled on the sofa watching *Hoarders* on TV. "The carpet layers are coming in three days." I handed him a box of extra heavy duty, 500-gallon trash bags. I could always depend on my meticulous mate to organize the household, so I imagined he would conduct a closet cleaning frenzy which might involve renting a bulldozer to reach the darkest corners. I envisioned the two of us kissing and laughing as we scooped up items from the closet floors, country music playing in the background, pausing occasionally to reminisce about a favorite shirt before folding it with love and placing it in a color coordinated container.

Instead, he threw me for a loop.

"No big deal." He yawned and scratched his stomach peeking out from under his red, Nebraska Huskers t-shirt. "I guess I'd better pick up my shoes and put them in the utility room." Standing up, he stretched before wandering off into our bedroom.

My jaw dropped as I followed after him. My husband owned four pairs of shoes. It would take him all of thirty seconds to clear out his side. "You mean you're not going to help me?" My heart pounded at the thought of tackling every closet alone.

He studied the three-foot length of clothes rod I'd allotted him when he'd moved in. "I don't wear half of these things." He snatched up an armful of shirts, jeans and a brand-new suit and stuffed them into a bag.

Panic rose in my throat, choking me. "But those are perfectly good clothes!" I felt my brow bead with sweat. "Why are you giving them away?"

"I've lost weight." He pulled up his shirt and showed me his newly deflated stomach. "Everything's fitting a little looser."

I looked at him incredulously. "What happens when you have a beer and gain it all back?"

He dismissed me with a wave of a hand. "*That'll* never happen."

He bent down and picked up a well-loved pair of cognac colored cowboy boots and weighed them in his hands.

My heart skipped a beat.

"These can go, too." He tossed the boots into the bag.

"But those were the boots you were wearing when we met!" I wailed.

"I have newer boots." He looked down at the tangle of shoes and shopping bags on my side of the closet floor, then up at my shelves, stuffed with purses and sweaters, and secret bins of love letters, at my closet rods crammed with a lifetime of clothes ranging from sizes 6 to 12, from every decade.

"When's the last time you wore this?" He pulled out the psychedelic sequined sheath I wore to my 10th high school reunion and added it to the bag.

"No!" I cried.

"Or this?" A cherry red patent leather jacket with gold epaulets and football player sized shoulder pads caught his eye. "Is this yours, or Michael Jackson's?"

"Don't you dare!"

He shook his head. "I can't help you if you're not willing to part with anything." He added the jacket to the other giveaways and slung the bag over his shoulder. "Good luck with the rest!"

The only thing I wanted to part with was him.

The counselor interjected in a soothing voice. "Sometimes we hang on to physical things because they remind of us happier times." She looked at us hopefully. "Perhaps we need to work on finding ways to move forward."

"Oh, I'll move forward." I shook her cool, slender hand at the end of our session. *Or he'll move out.*

We barely talked on the way back to the house.

"Couldn't you at least try getting rid of a few things?" he asked.

"I put some things in a bag."

He snorted. "You mean that small pile of maternity clothes?"

"Sometimes they're the only things that fit. Besides, there was more. A stained bathrobe...some night gowns." I held up my hand. "You know what, never mind. I'll take care of everything. I don't need your help."

For three days I bagged and sorted and hauled. Somehow, miraculously, by 3:00am on the morning the carpet installation was scheduled, I had dragged all the family skeletons out of the closets. Every Lego, every bobby pin, everything we'd ever swept under the rug was uncovered like an archaeological relic from the past and stored away for future generations to dissect.

At first, I bubble wrapped and packed each precious item in color coded bins, but when I ran out of boxes, time and patience, I resorted to stuffing armfuls of unrelated objects into Hefty contractor bags taller than I was. With no other choice, I lugged the giant masses into the only uncarpeted spaces in the house, the bathrooms, until every bathtub was filled with memories and treasures nobody treasured but me. My muscles ached. By the time the carpet layers arrived at 8am Friday morning, I could barely point them up the stairs.

Unfortunately, my husband followed behind them then called down to me. "What's with the trash bags in the bathtubs?"

I trudged back up the stairs and glared at him with bloodshot eyes as he inspected the contents.

"Now that wasn't so hard." He nodded in approval. "I can haul all this junk to Goodwill after lunch."

My heart skipped a beat. Goodwill! When he disappeared into our room to take a shower, I leaped into action. The attic was already full. I'd checked. He would see the bags in the garage, unless...

My husband took quick showers and I knew I had ten minutes, tops, to carry out my plan. I summoned up the last ounce of my strength and powered past the carpet layers who were chatting and planning their demo. I stormed into my son's bathroom first where I struggled to wrench a man-sized bag stuffed full of Little League trophies, game balls and team jerseys out of the tub. Wrapping both arms around the heavy, lumpy load, I danced the bag out of the room.

When I paused to catch my breath at the top of the stairs, the youngest, smallest carpet layer looked my way, pity in his eyes. Perhaps because of the way I was hunched over and wheezing, I reminded him of his aging grandmother. He approached me and gestured towards the bag. Then he gently transferred it out of my protective arms and into his own. He was tiny, and I could barely see the arches of his brows behind the massive load, but surprisingly strong--and agile. To my surprise, he ran down the stairs with the bag, as if it weighed no more than his sack lunch, deposited it by the garage door, and sprinted up for more. He gestured towards the others, and with grateful tears in my eyes, I watched the other two join in and form a caravan. With renewed hope, I fled down the stairs, threw open the door and raced to a tarp covered form parked in the far corner.

I couldn't remember the last time I'd noticed the vehicle, much less driven it. With no time to reminisce, I lifted the cobweb-covered cloth. The men gasped in unison and murmured their approval. Without stopping to admire the sleek body and candy-apple red paint of the vintage Mustang, I yanked open the passenger door. The familiar interior smelled of old leather and new beginnings, college football games and first loves, and I allowed myself for one glorious second to bask in the memories. Then we began wrestling the bags into the tight rear seat.

Like fire fighters rescuing victims from a burning building, we flew back up the stairs. I directed the men into the girls' bathroom next, where I'd salvaged sacks filled with well-loved American Girl dolls, their tiny outfits and miniature furniture. They grabbed the bags and hurried out of the room and down the stairs with me following close behind, cradling a basket of bitty babies in my arms. When the second load was safely stashed inside the car, I doubled over and caught my breath.

It was then I saw the bag from our closet my husband had carried out days before, leaning against the garbage can, ready to go out with the Friday trash. Peeking out of the top were his old boots, the ones we'd danced in, and romanced in, the pair he'd worn two years ago when we'd taken this giant leap of faith. I grabbed the boots, flung them into the front seat, slammed the door with a satisfying thud and pulled the tarp down.

I gave my new friends a thumbs up and they went back to the easier job of moving armoires. I found Cowboy lounging on the couch, curls damp from the shower, smug as a bug. I plastered an innocent look on my face and went into the kitchen to make a much-needed cup of coffee. With at least some of my treasures safely hidden, I could finally rest and let the installers do their work. I sat beside him, breathing in the aroma of my fresh cinnamon brew, feeling the tension in my shoulders start to relax.

He glanced over at me. "I hope you checked under the beds."

A chill traveled up my body. *Under the beds!* A wave of adrenaline propelled me up the stairs, but I was too late. Already the carpet layers had moved my son's wooden trundle. One of them was leering at a wrinkled 2005 Sports Illustrated Swimsuit edition, which he hurriedly shoved in his pocket when I burst into the room.

I noticed with alarm that the other two were beginning to take the girls' beds apart. I ran into my youngest daughter's room first, where teenaged dusty bunnies hopped over a collection of CDs, lost socks and a torn One Direction poster. In her older sister's room, I snatched a tiny training bra off the floor and paused to study a petrified Pop-tart pressed between the pages of a 2007 diary. Succumbing to temptation, I pried open the book, ignoring the carpet layer who was eyeing me with hands on his hips. *Wait until he has teenage daughters!*

Dear Diary, it read. *My mother needs to take a chill pill! I'm so sick of her yelling and threatening to ground me. As if! She totally thinks I cleaned my room today, but the minute I heard her coming up the stairs, I shoved everything under my bed.*

I knew it! Engrossed, I planted myself on the floor and read the next sentence. *Alex asked me to go to a movie this weekend, but Mom's so lame I can't even look at a boy until I'm an old lady like her...* My mouth dropped open and I turned the page. Before I could get to the juicy part, I heard the worker coming out of my son's room.

"Yo, Arturo, Hector," he called to the others. "*Vamos abajo.*"

I froze. While I was obsessing over the bottomless blackholes under my children's beds, I'd totally forgotten about my own. What shame was shoved under the massive sleigh bed I shared with my husband? What monsters lurked under the bed skirt? I wracked my brain, trying to remember what all I'd booted under there, and cursed the day I visited A1 Floors 4U.

I called my husband on the carpet. "Get your skinny abs off that couch! I need your help. Now!"

I thundered down the stairs, two at a time, and skidded into our bedroom, but it was too late. The men had hoisted our king-sized mattress onto its side and were peering down between the slats of the bed frame.

"*Ay, Chihuahua!*" one of them exclaimed, then all three turned to stare at my husband. The smallest one bristled and puffed out his chest.

My high school Spanish was rusty, but the translation was clear. The shag had hit the fan. It was then I realized I could save everything in this house, but I couldn't save myself.

"I told you to throw that crap away!" My husband glared at me, his face red. He looked at the men and threw his hands in the air. "Those aren't mine."

Their eyebrows shot up in unison and they turned to me.

My face burned. "They're just silly gifts." I smiled broadly, trying to diffuse the moment. "You know, for fun?" They stared at me blankly. I stuttered, trying to explain the couple's shower some friends had thrown for us before we got married, the gifts we'd received. "*Fiesta?*" I struggled in Spanish. "*Regalos?* From *amigos?*" I slapped my thigh to emphasize the hilarity of the situation while my husband seethed in the corner.

"This. Is. The. Last. Straw." He stormed out of the bedroom.

"They haven't even been opened!" I called after him. "I saved them because I was going to re-gift them." I got down on my hands and knees to scoop up the dust covered objects as the carpet layers watched with interest. "See, not even used." I waved one of the items in the air. "Not even once!"

The men looked at each other and muttered, "*Locos Gringos.*" Then they shrugged their shoulders and got back to laying the carpet.

The next day I found myself once again at the counselor's office. Apparently, my husband now had her number on speed dial.

"How did it make you feel?" she crooned to him in a soothing voice, "when the men found the fuzzy handcuffs, the leopard skin man's thong, the other..." she looked down at her notes, "things. That your *friends* gave you."

"Humiliated!" My husband clenched his fist.

"It wasn't the end of the world," I countered back, clutching my favorite pillow. Or maybe it was. I studied the sour expression on his face and allowed myself to imagine what I could do with his extra three feet of closet space. Where was the loving, fun man I'd married two years ago? For the first time in my life, I questioned if everything really was worth saving, including my marriage.

"I can see you two are in pain." She shook her head in sympathy. "May I suggest you try to reconnect by choosing a weekly ritual that is special to you?" She looked at us with hopeful eyes. "Perhaps take a walk, or share a cup of tea."

I began to believe someone besides my husband was crazy. "Like that's going to solve anything," I muttered under my breath, expecting him to walk out of the session in disgust.

"Actually," he said, "that's not a bad idea." He looked at me and nodded his head. "Your old Mustang. We should fix it up. Take it out for a spin."

"Yes!" the counselor said clapping her hands together.

"No!" I strangled the pillow I was holding and dropped it to the floor. "That old thing? It's a pile of junk. I was thinking of selling it." I dismissed the thought with a wave of my hand. "It's just taking up space in the garage."

The counselor looked at me with renewed interest. "I think we're making progress here."

"Are you crazy?" My husband's mouth dropped open. "That's a great car. It's vintage. You don't get rid of things like that."

I looked away. If only he knew my 80s car was filled to the brim with my 80s wardrobe and a decade worth of kid clutter, he'd march out of this room and out of my life. And so what if he did? Pride wanted me to let him go, to kick him to the curb along with all the belongings he didn't care about anymore.

Fortunately, my hoarding instincts kicked in soon after, and I decided to keep him.

My husband took my hand as we left the office. "It'll take a few days, but I'll get the old car up and running. We can go on rides every Sunday. Maybe have a picnic." His eyes were shining as we drove home. "You know, I'm really proud of how you cleared out those closets all by yourself."

I felt the weight of a dozen stuffed Hefty bags on my chest. "Yeah, well, about that..."

He pulled into our driveway and shut off the engine. We got out and walked into the garage. "What I'm trying to say is that I'm sorry. I was a real jerk." He paused and looked down at his feet. "You know, I kind of regret giving away those old boots." He walked up to the Mustang and with an exaggerated flourish, removed the tarp.

I held my breath.

"This side mirror looks loose. Bring me a screwdriver, would you? There's one in my toolbox."

Maybe being single again wouldn't be so bad, I tried to convince myself as a trudged across the garage. I'd be lonely at first, but I'd have the whole bed to myself. I'd get those three drawers back and I could finally watch *This Is Us* on Hulu without someone rolling their eyes on the couch next to me.

I opened his toolbox and a slip of powder blue caught my eye. I drew in my breath and reached for the familiar fabric. "My night gown." Puzzled, I clutched it to my chest and walked back towards my husband. "I gave this away. It makes me look fat."

His cheeks reddened and he shook his head. "I saved it. I love that nightgown on you." He reached for the door handle of the old sports car. "Now let's take a look inside."

"Wait!" I cried, but it was too late.

He flung open the door. "My boots!" He picked up the worn pair from the front seat like they were old friends and cradled them in his hands. "I gave these away. How'd they get in here?"

I looked into his green eyes, relieved to find the spark had come back into them. "I love those boots on you. We've gone through a lot in those boots." I took a deep breath and exhaled, feeling the stress of the last few weeks leave my body, and shuddered at how close we'd come to having the rug pulled out from underneath us.

We settled into the front seat and he looked down at a greenish blob on the footboard. "What the hell is that?"

"Frat party. TCU. 1982."

"This car's going to need new carpet." He glanced into the rearview mirror.

"Don't!" I cried, but it was too late.

"What's with all those trash bags in the back seat?" He twisted his body and began rummaging through them. "I knew it! As soon as I get this car running, we're driving it straight to Goodwill."

I leaned back onto the headrest and closed my eyes. I dreamed of Sunday drives with my husband in a fast car, picnics at sunset, our bare feet sinking into plush, sand colored carpet in a peaceful home. We had nothing but time on our side.

With a little luck, it would be days before he found what I'd stashed in those boots.

Romancing Ronni

The second my son graduated from college Alston got his first job. Robbing me of one last summer vacation with all my children, he packed up his new J. Crew work clothes and a month's supply of my special homemade Greek pastries (slice-and-bake Pillsbury chocolate chip cookies) and hopped into an old red Bronco. I stood on the driveway, heartbroken, crying and wiping my eyes, waving good-bye until he disappeared from sight.

Then I raced up the stairs, threw open his walk-in, shoved a few stray hangers into the corner and reclaimed his closet. A mom's got to do what a mom's got to do.

The truth was I missed him. We shared a goofy sense of humor and a love of cringe-worthy puns. Our laughter was longest and loudest after midnight when we grew especially delirious, long after the rest of the house had gone to bed. His daily phone calls indicated he missed me, too. He got a new dog who was friendly and faithful, I got a new husband. We both felt better—at least for a while.

A few months later he called me on the phone. "There's someone I want you to meet." His voice turned shy, "It's a girl. We've been dating."

"Oh!" My heart skipped a beat. He was so young, but it was inevitable a strong, kind, handsome young man would be swept off his Nikes by a sweet girl from work, or better yet, church.

"We met on Tinder."

Uh oh. Even I'd heard about the popular dating app with the sleazy reputation for promoting fast hookups. No mother wanted to hear her precious son was swiping left, or worse yet, right. Clearly, he was looking for love in all the wrong places and it was up to me to talk some sense into him before this hussy broke his Tinder heart.

"She's beautiful, smart, funny..." He sounded like he was reading directly from her bio, counting off her attributes one by one. I rolled my eyes. "She's from California, loves cooking and Chihuahuas. She graduated from your alma mater."

"*Hmmm.*" I examined my manicure, my interest slightly piqued, but I was still skeptical. Everyone on these dating apps sounded too good to be true. Someone was clearly catfishing my poor boy, taking advantage of his inexperience.

"And get this..." he paused for effect, "she's Greek!"

Then again, God works in mysterious ways.

The next weekend I took a road trip to Dallas. I had to meet this girl before she right swiped my son away for good. I dressed carefully. This girl could be the mother of my future grandchildren so I wanted to make a good impression. Nothing too flashy—black because it was slimming and sophisticated—a dress because I could wear it wherever we decided to go for dinner.

I pulled up to my son's Dallas apartment and lugged a plate full of cookies and my suitcase up three flights of stairs, huffing and puffing and sweating under the sweltering Texas sun. I'd barely knocked when the door swung open and a furry white tornado lunged at me, almost knocking me off my wedge sandals.

"Sinbad, sit!" My son, fresh out of the shower, hugged me with one arm and pulled his dog off me with the other. "He's just excited to see you. So am I." He grabbed a cookie before setting the plate on the counter, scooped up my suitcase, and disappeared into the bedroom. "Make yourself at home," he called to me.

Weary from the drive, I kicked off my shoes, tiptoed over a collection of dog bones and squeaky toys, and collapsed on his well-worn leather sofa. I sighed and closed my eyes. Maybe I'd have time to freshen up and take a little nap before we went out.

"Just don't sit on the couch!"

I jumped up.

The doorbell rang and he raced back into the room. "I didn't have time to vacuum the furniture." My son gestured for me to spin in a circle, took one look at my down covered backside and winced.

"Oh no!" I took a closer look at his fur-niture. What I'd mistaken for traditional, was woefully contempo-hairy. I craned my head over my shoulder in a futile attempt to survey the damage. The entire length of my black jersey dress was flecked with white fur from collar to hem. I slapped at my backside and clouds of white fluff flew off, only to fall like magnetic snowflakes right back on me again.

I slipped on the one shoe I could find, and was frantically hopping in a circle, brushing long white strands of dog hair off my body when an elegant Mediterranean beauty, dressed in flowy black chiffon, glided into the room. Stopping mid-swipe, I stared. Long, dark hair fell in soft waves, framing a smiling face. Green eyes fringed with long, black lashes, looked directly into mine as she held out a delicate hand in greeting. I blushed and offered a hairy hand in return. *Abominable Snowmom meets Greek Goddess*. With ladylike grace, she overlooked my half-shod feet and furry overcoat and shook my hand.

Even Sinbad was clearly stunned by her exquisiteness. He slowly approached, sat at her tiny feet, and looked up at her, steel blue eyes filled with puppy love. What remained of my wet, left sandal dangled from his mouth.

"Mom," my son announced proudly, "meet Ronni Bacocantpronounceopolous."

My mouth gaped open. Her last name was so long it could barely fit on the embossed wedding invitation I was silently designing in my head. I couldn't help myself—I was smitten. Maybe there was something to this online dating. Tinder or not, for me it was love at first site.

With the ease of online shopping, my son had found the perfect Greek girl. A *nifi!* I held out the cookie plate to my future daughter-in-law, she reached for the smallest one.

"Ba-co-cant-pronounce-at-all-polis..." The vowels rolled around in my mouth like Kalamata olives. "Now that's an authentic Greek name."

"Yes, it is." Ronni smiled and nibbled at her cookie. "But, I'm not Greek."

I inhaled sharply, almost choking on an imaginary pit. The opposite of a scream, this dramatic act of gasping had been employed by Greek mothers to express shock and disapproval since Eros hooked up with Psyche (against his mother's wishes). At the risk of swallowing their own tongues, my mom and yaya had perfected the technique. I'd learned from the best.

Ronni showed exactly how Greek she wasn't by not even noticing. She recited an epic tale about her father being only seven-years-old when his mother remarried a Greek man who adopted the little boy and raised him as his own. As a result, her father had a glorious Greek name, but not a drop of Greek blood pulsed through his body. Or his wife's. Or his daughter's. I shoved a cookie in my mouth to keep from crying over this modern Greek tragedy, and then reached for another.

Alston jumped in saying, "She had me fooled, too. But, get this, Mom. She speaks Greek!" He beamed. "I taught her myself."

I glanced at my son with suspicion. The few Greek words my children knew were the handful of ones I managed to retain from my Greek school lessons years ago. Dog, cat, boy, girl—I struggled to remember the simple words I'd taught them when they were little. I knew they'd also filed away more than one dirty word Nick, a naughty boy from class, had taught me when the teacher wasn't looking— the ones that now gave me great satisfaction when I was stuck in traffic, stubbed my toe, or discovered someone drank the last Diet Dr. Pepper in the fridge.

Alston nudged Ronni like she was a preschooler about to recite her ABCs, or rather, her Alpha, Beta, Gammas.

She scrunched up her face in concentration. *"Ehees,"* she began, looking up at me for approval, *"ena..."*

You have a... I smiled and nodded encouragement, wondering where this Greek lesson was going. Mentally, I filled in the blank as she searched for her next words. You have a... great son? You have a...shoe missing? Clueless, I looked at Alston, who was leaning on the counter, his face turning an alarming shade of red as his shoulders shook in silent laughter. I redirected my attention to Ronni whose face lit up as she remembered the last words.

"Megalo kolo!" she proclaimed with perfect pronunciation.

I dropped my half-eaten cookie back onto the plate. My son was in *megalo* trouble. I wanted to kick his *kolo*.

Alston fell to his knees, holding his stomach and Sinbad, thinking it was play time, pounced on him until the two of them disappeared in a cumulous cloud of fluff.

Ronni's forehead furrowed in confusion. "Did I say it right? It's. So. Nice. To. Meet. You."

This is definitely going in the toast I give on their wedding day. My heart melted when I saw the concern on her face. Even though I was the butt of the joke, I laughed until my eyes filled with tears. "Oh, Ronni..." I linked my arm in hers and led her to the couch. "You said it exactly right." I kicked off my remaining shoe and, following my lead, she slid hers off as well. I patted her knee. "It's very nice to meet you too."

We relaxed on the dog-earred sofa like old friends while I shared with her every embarrassing story I had about my son. How he once wore his sister's jeans to school by mistake and never noticed they barely grazed his ankles, or worse yet, had a tiny pink butterfly embroidered on the back pocket. I informed her that the polished, successful manager she was dating in the Peter Milar shirt dressed as a rootin' tootin' cowboy every Halloween for his first eight years, that he cried in Little League when he struck out at bat. I told her how he played with Beanie Babies in junior high, and how he feared the manhood eating toilet seat in his childhood bathroom.

Soon we were laughing so hard, neither of us cared that both of our *kolos* had collected coats of fur more impressive than Sinbad's.

When Alston was finally able to drag us off the couch to go to dinner, the three of us took turns brushing dog hair off of each other's backs. So what if we didn't share a common heritage? Tonight, our hair-itage, and our humor, would bond us. Furever.

The rest of the night we focused on our similarities instead of our differences. Ronni and I both liked frozen margaritas with salt, Broadway shows, and any song by Frankie Valli. We loved girl power and happy hour, spring flowers, and cherry sours.

Most importantly, we both loved my son.

I sat across the booth from the young couple at dinner and watched them interact. My heart swelled at how my son's arm draped comfortably across Ronni's shoulder, at how she smiled up at him, her face glowing, when he talked. It was too soon to know if this match was destined for happily ever after or just happily right now. It was all Greek to me. But tonight, the margaritas were cold, the salsa was hot, and love was in the air. And I was going to sit back and enjoy every Tinder moment.

Mind, Body & Soul Sister

For most of my life I've been a fitness fanatic. If there was something to kick, pedal or punch, I was there three times a week. I'd tried almost everything from Abs to Zumba. But my best friend, Celeste, runs circles around me. She enters marathons for fun, curly red hair bobbing to the beat of her custom playlist. Whether she's running to something, or from something, is a mystery to me. Our sweaty sisterhood works out because I stay out of her way until she's gotten her seven miles in and can justify meeting me at El Patio for blue margaritas.

"Running's not enough anymore," Celeste said while salting a basket of chips the waiter just placed on our table. "I need to cross train."

I wondered what my fit friend, a vision in Lululemon, was up to now, some plan I might want no part of, most likely. From middle school to middle age we'd sweated through life together, closer than most sisters.

"Now that we're in our fifties, we need to think about staying balanced and limber." She dipped a chip into a bowl of warm queso.

I'd give my right thigh for her thyroid. The truth was, the fit in my fifties was fizzling. I still worked out regularly, unless I was too tired, busy or not in the mood. I prided myself on being in shape, even if it was an oval one, and couldn't be blamed if people were jealous that I could eat whatever I wanted and still gain weight.

"So, I signed us each up for yoga classes." She waited until I stopped choking. "I'm free Tuesday or Thursday next week. Are you flexible?"

Was I? I couldn't remember the last time I'd touched my toes. But I'd bend over backward for my best friend, and yoga class meant we'd have a healthy excuse to get together.

"Sure," I lied, "I'm flexible."

The following Tuesday I met Celeste at Haute Yoga for You. She showed up in a soothing shade of sage, dressed in the latest yoga pants and a crop top from Sweaty Betty. I tugged self-consciously at my Gap sweatpants and followed her into the building.

"Is it just me, or is it hot in here?" My face felt flushed like it did on the rare occasions when I opened my oven door. "It must be over two hundred degrees. Let's come back after they fix the A/C." Through the steam I could see women the size of asparagus spears wilting from the heat.

Celeste whispered, "It's Bikram. Hot yoga." She claimed a spot in the center of the room and unrolled her mat. "And it's only a hundred and five degrees."

The instructor handed me a mat. Then she greeted the class with a bow and signaled for us to sit. A few women and one over-achieving male folded their legs into the lotus position. Celeste exhaled and gracefully crossed her legs.

Criss-cross applesauce! I commanded my long limbs to cooperate, but they stuck out stiffly in front of me. My fellow yogis progressed into the prayer pose. I muttered a prayer myself, grabbed my calf and pulled it close, managing to get one foot near the vicinity of my crotch. I caught my terrifying reflection in the mirror. Hair frizzed from the humidity, face red from the heat, I looked like a demon from the fiery pits of hell. The instructor frowned. I was already posing a problem.

Women (wispy as willows) bent into unspeakable shapes. I fought to mimic their moves. The only thing I'd stretched lately was the truth, and I struggled to touch my knees, much less my toes. I glanced at Celeste who appeared to be licking her navel.

"Relax," the instructor suggested. "Listen to your body."

My hungry stomach growled deeply in reply.

She took us through a series of animal poses. We arched like cats, sagged like cows, curled like cobras and humped like camels. We did things no self-respecting dog would do. When she instructed us to balance on our elbows and toes, I amazed myself by hovering over the floor like the others. She'd barely nodded her approval when my body, rotten to the very core we were trying to strengthen, collapsed from the strain. *After all I've done for you, this is the planks I get?* I landed face down on my borrowed mat, which after cooking for an hour at 105 degrees, emitted the comforting smell of stale Fritos.

Giving up, I rolled over and lay flat on my back, imagining myself at happy hour. I took a deep breath and exhaled, feeling the weight of my body melt into my mat. Calm covered me like a blanket and I closed my eyes.

So peaceful, I didn't hear the instructor patter up in bare feet.

"This pose of total relaxation is the most challenging of all." She paused. "This is the most perfect example I've ever seen of the corpse pose." My eyes fluttered open and I saw she was pointing at me. "Only the most advanced yogis can connect their mind, body and soul this way." Her dewy face beamed down at my impeccable form.

Minutes later I floated out of the room.

"Where are you going?" Celeste sprinted to keep up with me.

"I've got to run."

"Really?" Her eyes lit up.

"To Lululemon. I need clothes for class. And a yoga mat. The ones here smell like corn chips."

Celeste wrinkled her nose. "I don't think it's the mat."

"Karma will get you for that."

She followed me to the parking lot. "Same time Thursday, then?"

I smiled as she got into her car. We weren't getting any younger, but with a little meditation and a lot of dedication, my zen twin and I would flex our way through our fifties. I couldn't wait for our next yoga class. Now that I'd mastered the corpse pose, I was dying to go back.

With Celeste's help, one day I might even be able to touch my toes.

Is It Just Me, Or Is It Shawarma in Here?

Our church group trip to Israel was no vacation. This was made clear to us by our tiny, tyrannical tour guide, Katarina, who was not above employing militaristic tactics to keep us marching forward when all we wanted to do was pause long enough on the Via Dolorosa to take in the exotic sights and sounds of the old marketplace.

"Move along! Move along!" the sixty-something tour guide snapped at us, clapped her hands twice and stomped a foot. "This is a pilgrimage," she shrieked in a heavy Greek accent, "not a vacation." When a bolder female tourist dared to slow down, American dollars in hand, long enough to purchase an olive wood nativity scene from a vendor on the street, the tour guide's voice cracked like a whip on the cobblestone road, "No shopping! No *shopping!*"

To make matters worse, we were expected to continue this grueling spiritual journey straight through lunch. There was no time to break for a boring kebab when there were monasteries to visit and relics to relish. At first, I welcomed skipping meals, praying the first miracle we witnessed would be my losing five pounds. But the lack of food made me see visions, instead. Was that a heavenly light at the end of the tunnel, or a platter of hummus at the end of the buffet line? Was I hearing a divine message, or was that just my husband Cowboy's stomach growling again?

Seasoned traveler that I was, I knew to sneak food from the breakfast buffet to tide us over until dinnertime, swiping small, hard rolls with slices of cheese and sliding them, wrapped in paper napkins, into my purse. I borrowed bagels for my backpack and pilfered pita for my pockets. Hoarding food was in my genes (and now in my jeans) and Yaya, whose giant patent leather purse had always been stuffed with enough cracker packets and Melba toast to feed the masses, would have been proud of my ingenuity. I imagined the feast Jesus could have created with five fuzzy rolls and two slightly stiff sardines.

The forced fast was quickly turning the people of our peaceful pilgrimage into a pillaging posse. Lacking the basic comforts of home (like real diet Coke, cute shoes, and lunch) threw us into survival mode and tempers were taut. Even bottled water was scarce, which was just as well, since there was no bathroom on the bus and the fear of having to pee hung over us like humidity.

The poor travel conditions affected us all, but my Aunt Evelyn, who hadn't been on an airplane in 35 years, was the first martyr to suffer. It was the second day of the trip and we were riding in Bus #1 down a winding, mountainous road. Already that day she had lost her jacket, her sunglasses and a wide brimmed straw hat.

"Is she always like this?" A disgruntled man scowled and handed me her cheetah print scarf that he'd found on the ground outside the monastery.

"I'm not sure." I shrugged. "I only see her twice a year at holidays." I was puzzled, too. The aunt I knew, an avid baker and animal activist who boldly breezed into our family gatherings carrying plates full of rich homemade chocolate desserts, was a far cry from the anxious, disorganized woman who'd followed me on this trip.

We had just left Mt. Tabor, the site of Jesus' transfiguration when Evelyn began going through a less glorious transfiguration of her own. She started off that morning stylishly dressed, energetic and eager to witness a miracle. By afternoon she was minutes away from a meltdown instead.

"I hope I don't get motion sick." Evelyn rustled around in her backpack until she found a container of Dramamine and popped a few pills into her mouth. She shook the bottle near my ear. "Don't you want one? It would be terrible to get sick on the bus."

I shook my head and concentrated on staring out the front window, craning my head to see past our priest, who was seated in front of me.

"I mean, don't these twists and turns make you dizzy?" Evelyn poked her head through the space between the seat I shared with Cowboy. "I probably shouldn't have taken those pills on an empty stomach."

We bounced along in the bus for a few minutes in blissful silence.

"I'm starting to feel sick." Evelyn fanned herself with a map of the Sea of Galilee. "Do you feel sick?"

I'd felt fine before she mentioned it.

The bus lurched left and right; I focused on the yellow line in the middle of the road to get my mind off the somersaults my own stomach was performing. I dug in my purse and excavated a lint covered roll. "Eat this." I threw the baked good over my shoulder to my aunt. "It'll make you feel better."

Evelyn nibbled on the bread for a moment. Then she gasped and began rummaging around on the floor, tossing her belongings like a huge Greek salad onto the empty seat beside her. "Oh no!" She reached through the seats and grabbed my shoulder. "My purse. It's missing! I had it at the monastery and now it's gone."

Cowboy growled under his breath while I steeled myself, then swiveled around in the cramped seat to face her. "Evelyn, try to stay calm. Let's think about where you had it last."

"I might have left it in that horrible bathroom, the one without toilet paper." She moaned, her face turning white. "Or on that shuttle bus we got on with all those grumpy Romanians." Sweat formed on her forehead. "Help me find it! I'm too sick to move."

I groaned. My dream of a drama free vacation was disappearing as fast as beef kabobs on an all-you-can-eat buffet. I performed acrobatics to dislodge my body from the seat I shared with Cowboy and dug through the pile of belongings on the seat next to hers— sweaters in case it was cold, sunscreen in case it was hot, a fancy camera that couldn't hold a charge. It was no wonder she kept losing things. She'd packed everything but her well-stocked kitchen pantry and whatever didn't fit in her massive suitcase, she carried in her bare hands.

I grabbed her backpack and searched through every pocket, unearthing enough hand sanitizer to disinfect every hand on the bus and enough tissue to wipe every tushie. My fingernails raked across something large and hard at the bottom of the bag. I whipped my hand out and examined my nails, now dirty and brown. Instinctively shifting into motherhood drive, I brought my fingers to my nose and sniffed.

"Baking chocolate," Evelyn said grabbing for her backpack, reaching into it, breaking off a chunk and swooning as it melted on her tongue. "For medicinal purposes. Can you look under all the seats? Maybe someone picked it up by mistake."

I glanced at the other passengers wedged into each bus row, thighs spreading uncomfortably into the aisles. The grim Greek faces of half-starved church council members, deacons and priests stared back at me. I had grown up and grown older with most of these people. They knew my parents and my grandparents and my children. But my spiritual-but-not-religious aunt and my new Irish Catholic but evasively evangelical husband were outsiders, loose cannons on this bus. My goal was to keep them from blasting through my reputation as a semi-regular Christmas and Easter, once-a-month when I didn't have too many margaritas on Saturday night, church-going pillar of the community.

I set my mouth in a stubborn line. I may have been younger than my absent-minded aunt, but I was twice her size. Although I would crawl on my hands and knees to kiss the spot where Christ was crucified, I drew a hard line at dropping into a downward dog in the middle of a speeding bus, in front of God and my 5th grade Sunday school teacher, even if I was wearing my comfortable new Athleta travel pants.

"Aunt Evelyn, take some deep breaths. It'll be ok. The most important thing is that you have your passport." A crazed look came over her face. My stomach did a flip. "Where's your passport?"

Her eyes grew wild with emotion. "In my purse! Everything—all my money, my credit cards, my passport, my *life*—is in that purse."

Breakfast bubbled up inside me as I grasped the severity of the situation. I reached across the aisle and tapped Katarina on the shoulder. "I hate to bother you, but we have a slight problem."

Katarina ignored me and continued yelling into her cell phone, "I don't care what time your hotel dining room closes. I have seexty hungry people and you're going to feed them." Her face turned as red as her disheveled hair. "And eet better be good food, too, not some cold cra..." she turned to look at me and clicked her phone shut mid rant.

I took a deep breath. "One of the passengers seems to think she misplaced her purse," I whispered to avoid alerting the rest of the bus and calling unwanted attention to us.

Katarina's eyes grew as wide as Kalamata olives. She bolted to a standing position. "Who? What passenger?"

"The woman behind me." I swallowed. "My aunt."

The tour guide moaned. "This eesn't good. This ees *not* good. What was een her purse? Her money? Her credit cards?"

I nodded. "And her passport."

Katarina wailed and tore at her hair. Then she snarled at the driver in a demonic voice, "Stop the bus!"

The driver swerved in surprise. "I cannot pull over!" he shouted in broken English. "I am on a toll way."

The sudden movement woke all the passengers from their low blood sugar comas. A woman across from me gasped and clutched the cross around her neck as a collection of water bottles rolled down the aisle.

"Is it desert bandits?" the woman asked, her voice trembling.

"Maria, we're not in the desert," a man answered. "We're on a freeway in Nazareth, for Pete's sake. Look..." he pointed out the window. "There's an H&M store."

Evelyn began dry heaving. "I'm going to be sick!"

Muttering something to Jesus under her breath, Katarina leaped from her seat and sprang into action. She grabbed a plastic bag from the overhead bin and thrust it at Evelyn, then snatched up her cell phone and pounded in some numbers. The whole bus could hear her yelling in Greek to a monk from the Transfiguration Monastery.

Thanks to the Friday night Greek school I attended each week when I was a little girl, I could decipher almost every other word of her passionate plea. Woman. Purse. Crazy. Please. Some of the others on the bus, however, understood it all.

"A woman lost her purse?" the man who had earlier found my aunt's scarf on the ground growled. He stared daggers at Evelyn and pointed an angry finger at her. "Not you again!"

"If we turn back now to go get it, we'll miss dinner, too!" yelled another. "The brochure promised shawarma."

"And what about shopping tonight?" a woman's shrill voice echoed from the back of the bus. "You promised to take us to your favorite store and now we won't have any time."

We were minutes away from a mutiny and I looked to the priest for help; he stared straight ahead like a religious statue, clearly unwilling to get involved in the bedlam on the bus. I glanced at my aunt, frazzled and frail, wearing a thin cardigan, hunched over her plastic bag dry heaving while the others complained. Indignation roared up inside me. Where was the holy in this Holy Land trip? Who were the pilgrims on this pilgrimage? My aunt was about to be sacrificed to the lions and I didn't have a prayer to save her. So I did what any good niece would do.

I got down on my knees— and looked under the seat.

My simple act of kindness spread like hummus on pita and soon a symphony of sixty pairs of arthritic knees could be heard creaking and popping as every passenger on the bus knelt down and searched every row.

And came up empty-handed.

I looked at Evelyn and shook my head. The money and credit cards we could replace, but the passport was her ticket to travel, the key to unlock the mysteries and miracles in Egypt the next day where we'd visit the burning bush and Moses' well. More importantly, it was her gateway to returning home where she reigned.

"It's ok." Evelyn took a deep breath. "I've prayed about it and I know I'm going to find my purse." She stood up, unbuttoned her sweater and shrugged it off her shoulders. "Is it warm in here, or is it just me?"

"I don't believe it." The man across the aisle rolled his eyes and nudged his wife with his elbow. He jabbed a crooked finger at Evelyn. "What's that hanging across your shoulder? It wouldn't be a *purse* would it?"

I stared at her, my mouth gaping open.

Evelyn looked up to the heavens and cried, her face beaming with joy. "Oh thank you, thank you! I knew I'd find it."

Relief and irritation danced the *hora* through my body, jockeying for the lead. "Were you wearing it the whole time? Under your sweater?"

Minutes later, the bus pulled up to the hotel and everyone raced to raid the dinner buffet, except Katarina, who snuck off to the bar where I imagined she'd have more than one stiff drink. Evelyn exited last, eyes bright in search of the next miracle, walking briskly, the blue cloth purse strapped securely across her chest. Her determined pace said there was no time to lose with shawarma to sample and shopping to do.

I looked at my aunt and marveled at her determination. It was only day two and she'd lost her jacket, her sunglasses and her wide brimmed hat. She'd lost her purse and passport. She'd almost lost her cookies. However, she'd never lost her faith.

"Oh!" She paused and pointed to the corner where a dark-skinned man stood next to a camel, a small group of tourists surrounding him, cameras posed. "I'm going to ask him if I can ride it." She ran down the sidewalk, dropping her sweater along the way, and called back over her shoulder at me, "I mean, what have I got to lose?"

I walked down the block, admiring the pink and yellow stripes of color streaking across the foreign twilit sky, and stooped to pick up my aunt's sweater. I tucked it under my arm and strolled back to the hotel where the bus driver was waiting, holding a backpack.

"Someone left this on the bus." He grinned and shrugged his shoulders. "I thought maybe you'd know who it belongs to."

I unzipped it just to be sure and smiled when I saw the slightly soft bar of chocolate inside. I broke off a piece and placed it in my mouth, savoring the bittersweet taste of home. If I squinted, I could just make out Evelyn's thin form balancing regally on the camel's back, glowing brightly as she rode off into the sunset.

Daddy Doolittle

My dad has an animal magnetism that is irresistible. Like a disheveled Dr. Doolittle wearing a stained undershirt instead of a top hat, his inner spirit seems to send out subliminal signals, driving every species wild. Dogs obey him, cats approve of him, birds flock to him as if his pockets are filled with breadcrumbs and seeds. Every creature, large and small, instinctively knows my dad is good for a quick meal, a loving pat, and a warm place to sleep.

Apparently, my mother couldn't resist him either, which may explain why I was born nine months after their wedding night, more or less.

My dad, who grew up in Greece, had pets instead of toys. Besides the one ball the village children shared, made from a blown-up sheep bladder, toys were a luxury he and his brothers did without. Instead, they played with baby goats, birds they trapped and a mean mule named Marko who refused to allow anyone but my father to ride him.

While my dad had a way with animals, my mom stayed *away* from animals. She grew up with tea parties and Madame Alexander dolls. Seldom straying outdoors into the Houston humidity, one of her earliest exposures to wildlife was when she was four-years-old and her grandmother's chicken chased her across the backyard, squawking and pecking at her skinny white legs. As a result, she developed a phobia to anything with wings, and even as an adult, would hold her head and duck when a bird flew overhead. A perfectionist, she disliked anything that pooped, peed or dropped food on the floor, with the grudging exception of her family.

Nevertheless, proving you can take the man out of the old country, but you can't take the old country out of the man, my dad never stopped trying to convert his suburban American ranch style into a Greek village farmhouse. Growing up, our home resembled a zoo, housing a variety of strays we were ill equipped to care for.

"Oh, Albert!" My mom's hands flew up to cover her head as she glared in horror at the latest offensive beast he'd dragged home. "What's that? You know how I feel about chickens!"

"It's a rooster. You won't even know it's here." My dad, not to be hen pecked, brushed past her, the frightened farm fowl clutched in his arms. "Look at this beauty! No more sleeping through the alarm clock around here. We won't even *need* alarm clocks!"

Dad got the rooster from a man named Pappas who had found an egg while on a family trip to Bandera, tucked it into his pocket and coddled it in an incubator at his palatial home in Memorial. It was all fun and games as they waited for it to hatch, his children getting a front row view of the miracle of life, but the fuzzy chick grew into a raging lunatic who lunged at anyone who came near him. Dad, always up for a challenge, thought it would be a great idea to relocate the rowdy rooster to our backyard and offered to take the cock off Pappas' hands.

Apparently, the rooster didn't like our house any better and he let the whole block know. My brother and sister and I slept through all the cock-a-doodle doing, but the neighbors didn't. A week later, Dad's feathered friend flew the coop. Or at least that's what we were told.

A menagerie meandered in and out of my childhood, few animals staying long enough to create a lasting bond with me or my little brother and sister. My yaya was left to care for my dad's strays long after we lost interest in them. We had baby ducks in our swimming pool that made such a mess they had to be surreptitiously relocated to the pond at Herman Park. Bunnies bounced in and out of our lives while a fish tank grew murky in the corner of our living room.

One day my dad pulled his Cadillac into the driveway, honked the horn for us to come outside, and jumped out, a huge, my-wife's-going-to-kill-me grin on his face. He opened the back door of the car and reached inside, struggling with something, muttering Greek curse words under his breath. "I'm going to take you to the glue factory you stubborn old..." Moments later, he disentangled a large mammal from the back seat and led it out with a rope. He brushed the pony's tangled mane out of its glassy eyes then turned to us and smiled broadly.

My mother shielded her eyes against the bright sun. "Oh, Albert." Her jaw dropped to the driveway. "That's not a *horse*, is it?"

He laughed, scooped up my little sister and plopped her on the animal's faded brown back. "It's a pony! From Kiddie Land. Poor thing's so old it can't chew oats, but he's got a lot of years left in him." He led the pony through the front yard, my sister waving to the cars speeding by our house on Hillcroft Ave.

"How on earth?" My mother peered into the back seat of the car. "Albert! Where's the backseat?"

A pile of steamy hot pony poop sat where the leather seats used to be. Mom gagged and stormed back into the house while the rest of us horsed around and around on the lawn, our one trick pony creating a path in the grass that would last much longer than he did.

The only pet that passed family approval and stayed around long enough to earn a name was Zorba, a green, one-eyed parrot my dad brought home when I was in junior high school. Zorba perched in his cage in the corner of the living room and eyed us suspiciously as we gathered around, offering him sunflower seeds and tiny pieces of fruit.

"Hello? Hello! *Hello*," my dad coaxed and cajoled in various inflections, trying to engage our new pet in a conversation. "The man who sold him to me said the damn thing's supposed to talk."

"Polly want a cracker?" I stuck half a saltine between the bars of the cage and shook it at the bird but he turned his cloudy bad eye to me, ignoring my offering.

"His name's Zorba," my sister reasoned, "maybe he only talks Greek!"

My dad nodded and tried again, speaking louder as if our new-feathered family member was deaf as well as half blind. "*Ella tho!* Come here. *Ella tho.*"

Zorba cocked his head.

"I think we're getting somewhere. *Ella tho.*"

The whole family leaned in closer, certain their newest pet was going to utter his first word. Zorba ruffled his feathers, puffed out his lime green chest and opened his beak. "Squaaawk!" His tiny black tongue vibrated as he screeched. He chuckled as we jumped back from the cage, my mother clutching the top of her head, suffering from sudden PTSD, Parrot Traumatic Stress Disorder. "Squaawk!" His one eye winked as the high-pitched shrieks rang through our ears.

The following Sunday, my grandmother and I were up early getting ready to go to church, while the rest of the family slept in. I always seemed to be running around frantic, searching for a Sunday dress or a missing patent leather pump. On this particular morning, the dress I wanted to wear was wrinkled and I knew Yaya would come to the rescue and iron it for me. I tiptoed through the living room so I wouldn't wake up Zorba who was still asleep, his head tucked into his chest peacefully as if his body were a feather bed. The last thing I wanted to do was wake up the crazy bird who would in turn rouse the entire family with ear-splitting screeching.

I knocked softly on Yaya's bedroom door. She poked her head out, and seeing the coast was clear, stepped into the living room wearing only her black, nylon full-length slip.

Zorba caught the swish of satin out of the corner of his good eye and came alive, his body stretching to an erect six inches. He jumped up and down on his perch as he followed Yaya's form floating in front of him. Then he opened his beak and wailed out a wolf whistle that could have awakened the dead, or at least my family, catcalling my grandmother like she was a Greek Jane Russell passing a construction site at lunchtime.

"Wheeet-whooo!" the bird whistled, shaking his cage. "Wheeet-whooo!"

Yaya blushed and whirled around to glare at him as he hopped from one foot to another.

"Wheeet-whooo!"

By now the entire family had stumbled out of their beds to see what all the ruckus was about.

"Shake it baby!" the bird shouted in a husky, deep voice. "Shake it!"

Yaya, realizing she was dressed in just her slip in front of the entire family, raced to the safety of her bedroom and slammed the door. I looked down at my wrinkled dress and wondered if we were going to make it to church that day.

"Ella tho," Zorba crooned from his cage. "Polly want a dollar?"

My mom, still holding her hair with one hand, hit my dad in his beefy bicep with the other. "Albert! Just where did you find this parrot?"

My dad grinned from ear to ear before turning to go back to bed. "I told you that bird could talk."

Zorba became a feathered family fixture after that. Because we were too scared to give him away for fear he'd repeat all our secrets, he ruled the roost from his golden cage for years, keeping one eye on us as we grew up and grew older. When at last he streaked off to the great strip tease in the sky, it was hard to tell who was sadder—my dad who had lost a Greek speaking parrot pal, or Yaya who had to resort to the neighborhood Walmart for male attention.

One by one, me, my sister and my brother left for college. Dad no longer had an excuse to bring animals home. Once a sanctuary for strays and underdogs, the zoo on Hillcroft closed its admission gates. Like an inmate released from prison, for the first time in over twenty years, my mother ventured out into her backyard. But as soon as the first grandchildren came along, my dad was back in business.

As much as I loved dropping my kids off at my parents' house for the eager, free babysitting they provided, I dreaded picking them up for fear of what they'd be lugging home.

An overgrown child himself, Dad would slip off with the children as soon as they arrived, piling them into his ancient Cadillac which now had a functioning, but different color, backseat. Deprived of playthings in his youth, he showered his grandchildren with piles of picture books and towers of toys. A typical Friday night consisted of him stuffing the kids full of Baskin Robbins ice cream *and* donuts from Shipley, and then letting them run rampant through Toys R Us, throwing whatever they wanted into the cart.

"Oh, Albert!" My mother would shake her head when the crew returned to the house sticky and sweaty and smiling brightly, dragging shopping bags behind them. "Where have you been?"

"Fifth amendment," my dad would answer back, stashing twenty-dollar bills into the pockets of the children's jeans as they tore into the bags.

"Fifth amendment!" the children would repeat in unison.

As a result of these covert missions, our house was bursting with Barbies and Beanie Babies, building blocks and balls. At first, my husband and I good-naturedly accepted the toys as tokens of love from a doting grandfather, but when the stuffed animals turned into the unstuffed variety, we had to draw the line.

"Kids, we don't have room for pastel-colored fuzzy chicks." Guilt clenched my gut as my children and their grandfather eyed me expectantly then sadly hung their heads. "But we'll visit them at Poppy's house every week."

Mom, a bitter critter sitter, held her tongue. But she shot my dad a look and shook her head before kissing us all goodbye. Although the kids sniffled all the way home, just like they did the week before when we raced off leaving three smelly red-eared slider turtles behind, visiting my mom and dad's house was the highlight of our week for many years. Under the directorship of Daddy Doolittle, the Hillcroft Haven for Homeless Pets thrived until the last granddaughter gave up toys for boys.

If it's hard to watch your children grow up, it's even harder to watch your parents grow older. Without his grandchildren and wayward pets, my dad made a valiant effort to entertain himself indoors, watching old westerns on TV with the volume blaring and studying the Houston Chronicle from front page to back. He read the entire collection of Louis L'Amour paperbacks while sitting at the kitchen table in his favorite ribbed tank undershirt.

Overjoyed to have her yard back, my mother planted plats of petunias and rows of roses. She transformed her patio into a page out of Home and Garden magazine.

One pleasant spring evening, I arrived unannounced bearing their favorite dessert, a double-layer coconut cake. Mom invited me to sit outside with her and my dad on the new patio furniture. I grinned as I watched him fidget on the hard wrought iron chair beside her, stretching and squirming to get comfortable while I sliced them both slabs of cake.

"Isn't it beautiful out here?" she sighed and admired the pristine, pet-free view. "I finally have the yard I've always wanted."

Dad nodded his head and whistled softly. The wind picked up and the trees rustled restlessly overhead. A red cardinal circled above, catching his eye. Several wrens resting on a branch flapped their wings.

Mom tasted her cake and blotted her lips with a napkin. "I wish the grandkids would come by to see how nice it looks."

Dad mumbled under his breath, took a bite of his piece and brushed the crumbs off his undershirt. A squirrel darted out from beneath some bushes and nibbled at the moist morsels, chirping to his buddies to check out the treat.

"I miss seeing them every week. Everyone's so busy now." She glanced over at my dad who was breaking off chunks of cake and tossing them to the family of squirrels who had congregated by his feet, chattering excitedly. Dad whistled again, more loudly this time, and a host of hummingbirds hurled past his ear, hovered over a red hibiscus plant and zipped back towards him again, narrowly missing my mom's perfectly coifed curls by mere inches. Reflexively, her hands flew to her hair and she ducked her head.

Sensing another animal argument brewing, I stood and walked towards the house asking, "Who wants coffee?" I called out to my parents but they ignored me, lost in their own little world.

I watched as my dad reached out and took her soft trembling hand in his warm, calloused one. "Look at those." He raised his chin at an old oak in the corner of the yard and made a soft cooing noise. "Doves." He scraped the remaining crumbs off his plate onto the ground in front of my mom's white sneakers and a pair of cream tipped birds whistled towards them and landed gracefully at her feet.

Mom flinched, but when the larger, more dominant bird bowed and nodded his head at the smaller one, she became fascinated. He serenaded his partner with a soothing love song, then the pair necked playfully before their beaks met in a tender kiss.

"They mate for life." My dad pulled my mother close and kissed her on the lips. "Just like us."

Pausing by a potted plant on the patio, I spied on my parents, my eyes misting with tears. Moments like this were why, even after failing at marriage, I still believed in forever.

"Oh, Albert," she sighed and took one last wistful look at her impeccable yard as the sun melted into pink and orange swirls, casting a rosy glow over her perfect piece of paradise. The birds and squirrels chirped and chattered with anticipation.

My dad smiled at her and cocked an eyebrow.

"One birdhouse, Albert. I *mean* it."

The doves cooed as if they understood. A soft smile formed on my mother's face and she leaned down and gently placed her cake plate, dusted with vanilla crumbs, in front of them. Dad squeezed her hand and my parents sat watching the lovebirds nibble the sweet feast off her good china long after the sun set over the house on Hillcroft.

THE ANIMAL WHISPERER

ALBERT THE GREAT

It's All Greek
to (23 and) Me

From the day I was born, my Greek parents did everything in their power to raise the perfect Greek-American girl. First, they baptized me in the Greek Orthodox church, the same one where they were married two years before. They hung tiny *mati* charms on my baby clothes to ward off the evil eye, and enrolled me in Orthodox Sunday school as soon as I could talk. After I had mastered the English language at the public school I attended, every Friday evening when my non-Greek friends were going to Brownie meetings or softball practice, my parents sent me to Greek school where Mrs. Thaskala crammed Greek nouns down my throat with a well-worn yardstick. Since we didn't speak Greek at home, and the only practice I got was in the class, I excelled at reading and writing the language, but still choked on all the words, except the dirty ones Nick, who sat behind me, whispered in my ear.

"The cat is black," Mrs. Thaskala spit out the words as if it disgusted her to have to pronounce them in English. Her dark eyes landed on me. "In Greek!"

I cringed and shrank at my desk, at a loss for words. Cat? I struggled to remember the vocabulary from our homework assignment.

"Skata," hissed Nick in my ear. "Cat is *skata.*"

Thankful for his help, I articulated the sentence to the class. *"To skata einai mavro."*

When Mrs. Thaskala's mouth dropped open and she pounded her yardstick on the tile floor, I suspected I was in trouble. When the other children howled with laughter, I knew I was. *"Gata!"* Mrs. Thaskala's screamed the word at the class. "No *skata!*" Her lips disappeared into a thin line as she pulled me from my desk and dragged me to the blackboard. *"To gata einai mavro!"* She thrust a broken piece of chalk into my hand and gestured for me to write the sentence on the board one hundred times as Nick snickered in the background.

Despite my protests, my parents forced me to attend Greek school for five years. Although I made a half-hearted attempt to master the language, if only so I'd know what my parents were saying when they were talking about me in Greek, the only person I ended up being able to converse with was Nick, and that was only if the topic of conversation was limited to black cats defecating.

My dad prided himself on being 100% Greek, possibly a descendent from Zeus. He had come over from the old country with his brothers when he was thirteen, enrolled in school, and taught himself English using flash cards during his lunch break. He worked as a bellhop after school, then as a delivery boy, and had perpetually red eyes from lack of sleep. He met my mother a few years later at Lamar High School and the rest was Greek history.

"Why did you choose Mom?" I grilled my father.

He looked at me as if I were crazy. "I knew she was a good Greek girl!"

"What if she wasn't good? What if she wasn't Greek?" I goaded him, but I knew the answer. He never would have considered her if she hadn't met his criteria.

As I grew older, it became apparent that I was being groomed for something special too—a good Greek boy.

My dad always lectured me whenever the entire family was crammed in his Kalamata-colored Cadillac, usually on the way to our favorite restaurant: The Great Greek.

"A good Greek boy will treat you right." My dad began every lecture about my future husband the same way. "He'll be from a good Greek family."

When I tried to argue with him from the backseat, he would turn up one of his Trio Belcanto eight-track-tapes until the whining bouzouki music drowned out my voice and any hopes I had of having blonde babies with my current crush from school, Donny Donaldson.

Years flew by. I cooked Greek food and spent summers in the Peloponnese. My best friends were good, Greek girls like me. I performed in Greek Independence Day celebrations against my will, and attended Greek conventions out of town.

I danced the *Zorba* at the Houston Greek Festival, arms outstretched, legs kicking faster and faster to the lively beat, lost in a circle of music and magic, as the excited crowd shouted, "Opa!" Meanwhile, I dated a succession of Greek boys my father hand-picked for me, but in spite of his best intentions and not so subtle threats, I married a boy with a questionable pedigree I met by the pool when I was in college.

I knew I should have listened to my father. Twelve years later, I ended up divorced with three children while my younger sister, Anne, was still happily married to Nick, my nemesis from Greek school.

Still, I never questioned who I was or where I came from. Greekness oozed out of my pores like extra-virgin olive oil.

All that changed the day my sister invited us over to her house to celebrate her 50th birthday. Although she had rebelled against our father in every other way, she dutifully married a Greek man and he'd prepared lamb in honor of her big day. Nick knew I hated the dish and served it at every family gathering.

"I have some exciting news!" My sister flipped a dark, glossy curl over her shoulder and waited until she had our undivided attention.

The hairs on the back of my neck sprang up in alarm. My little sister's big announcements usually meant big trouble. I swallowed a bite of Greek salad and waited.

She stood up and paused for effect. "For my birthday this year, Nick gave me the best gift."

I fought the urge to roll my eyes. *Every* year she got the best gift. Two birthdays ago, it was a two-week trip to Fiji. Last year it was a new sports car. I pursed my lips as everyone looked up at her expectantly.

"He had my DNA tested on 23 and Me." Her gaze traveled over us as she waited for the news to sink in.

I exhaled. This year's gift was underwhelming. I was surprised my brother-in-law would waste a hundred dollars to discover what we all already knew. We were 100% Greek. No spit could deny that.

I pitied the poor people in the DNA commercials who grew up believing they were German, wearing Lederhosen and chugging from steins as an *Oompah* band played in the background, only to have to trade in their biers for burritos when they discovered that by some twist of fate, they were Mexican instead. The commercial fades as the family, now donning sombreros, claps along with a festive Mariachi trio. I thanked the Greek gods that kind of identity crisis could never happen in our family.

My sister caught my father's eye and smiled as she said, "Of course, I'm mostly Greek."

My dad toasted her with his Diet Coke and went back to his roasted lamb.

"But the rest of the results are rather surprising." Her gaze settled on my mother, and she blurted out the news as if she'd won the lottery, "I'm thirty-nine percent Italian!" She pointed at me. "That means you're Italian, too!"

I nearly choked on the olive I was eating.

"Isn't that exciting?" My sister jumped up and down as if she had the patent for pasta. "We're Italian! Of course, it can't be from Dad's side." She waved a manicured hand at him. "He goes back to Alexander the Great. But, Mom?" She walked over to my mother who wore the horrified expression of a woman who'd just been caught pinching the statue of David's behind. "How much do you know about Yaya?"

My mother waved her hands over her plate. "*Shhh.*" She glanced nervously at my dad who was adjusting his hearing aid. If her blood were tainted with even one drop of Italian dressing, the last person who must know was my father.

I could think of 23 reasons why my sister should drop this senseless talk, but she ignored my mother and babbled on. "We should explore this exciting new heritage," she gushed on, "embrace the traditions, food and music of our rich, new culture."

I put down my fork and squirmed uneasily. "Italian?" The word felt foreign on my tongue, and left a bitter taste in my mouth. Suddenly my genes didn't fit. With one drop of spit, my sister had wiped out life as I knew it.

I squinted at my mother as if seeing her for the first time. I'd always bought my mom's excuse that she couldn't cook, but maybe this could explain why we had been raised on SpaghettiOs and Tortino pizza rolls instead of pastitsichio like all the other Greek kids.

My heart welled with emotion. Although I'd spent all my life complaining about being Greek, defending my big, loud family, and explaining to the world that we didn't celebrate Easter a week late just to buy half-price candy, I loved being Greek. I couldn't imagine NOT being Greek. I didn't know the first thing about being Italian! Now, like one of those pathetic people on the ancestry commercials, I'd have to change hats mid-life, at least 39% of the time.

My brother-in-law brought out a huge slab of tiramisu to celebrate. "Happy Birthday, Annie! It's sweet and Italian, just like you." He beamed as she leaned down to blow out the candles.

She's only thirty-nine percent sweet. My mind wandered and I tried to envision myself as a young Italian girl. In my fantasy I was a sultry, hot-tempered Sophia Loren look-a-like with long, wavy hair, lips that could melt butter, and breasts the size of warm calzones. My new Italian family was just as large and loud as my Greek one, but I imagined a massive metal pot on the stove boiling with pasta and sauce, my mother in an apron, slapping my brother on the side of the face when he talked back to her, then immediately kissing the same spot.

We'd be Catholic, and connected, and a collection of gorgeous Italian boys would ignore me while they dated pretty blonde girls without overprotective parents, saving me for later. After all, my godfather was *the* Godfather. We'd buy our clothes in Milan and vacation in Venice where serenading gondoliers would lead us through the canals singing *Volare* in velvety voices. They'd know us all by name since my father was an excellent tipper.

"And here's a little Italian something for my little Italian wife." Nick whipped out a shopping bag with a designer name emblazed across it. He tapped his phone and the first notes of *That's Amore* played sweetly in the background.

I shook my head. After all these years he was still full of *gata*.

"*Ooh!*" my sister squealed and jumped up from the table. "Something from Gucci!" She pulled out a tote bag stamped with the iconic logo.

I could smell the irresistible scent of Italian leather from across the table.

"But there's more!" exclaimed Nick. "Look inside."

My sister unzipped the bag, peeked into it, and pulled out a folder from one of the pockets. "Oh my God!" She covered her mouth with her hand. "Is this what I think it is?"

"Tickets for two to Italy!" Nick hugged her and twirled her around. "So we can trace your roots."

I looked over at my dad who had taken out his hearing aid altogether, and was banging it on the table in frustration. Roots were important, but as long as the soil was good, did it really matter where we were planted? Suddenly, I didn't care about the dirt my brother-in-law was digging up. Our family tree was thriving because of its strong trunk, my father. And thanks to my mother, the loving branch that reached out and held us together, we would continue to grow long into the future.

I pushed back my chair and stood to face my sister. "I have to go."

"So soon? We're going to play Bocce..."

I waved at her over my shoulder as I made my way to the door. Dean Martin's sultry voice followed me out onto the street, crooning about a moon hitting his eye like a big pizza pie. I never did understand that line.

Taking a deep breath, I paused to gaze up at the fat, full moon above, marveling at the thousands of stars twinkling overhead. It was a perfect night for a *Godfather* marathon and Netflix was making me an offer I couldn't refuse.

Suddenly, I had a strange craving for a pepperoni pizza.

THE END
(for now)

Acknowledgements

*Yaya's **Big Black Purse*** would still be a dream hanging in the corner of my closet if it weren't for the individuals and writing groups who supported me along the way.

This collection of fiction is lovingly based on my Greek life and the people who make it a rich, fulfilling one. My family and friends are my inspiration and the heart of my stories, and through laughter and tears, make life worth writing about. They grew up and grew older with me, sharing every chapter from middle-school to motherhood to middle-age. I want to thank them for allowing me to share our memories, mishaps and misadventures—and for putting up with my corny puns.

Home is where my story begins. Thank you to my children, Alston, Kati and Kristina, who encouraged me to write this book, and are still talking to me even though I didn't change their names. (They also want me to reiterate that this is a work of fiction and any resemblance to actual persons, living or dead, is purely coincidental.) Thank you to my wonderful parents for giving me and my brother and sister a solid, loving foundation, and for showing our family what happily ever after is all about. Even though they forced me to go to Greek school and wouldn't allow me to shave my legs until I was twelve, I wouldn't have traded my childhood for anything—even a more normal one.

I owe a huge thank you to the members of my Houston Writers Guild critique group. Each Thursday morning, Alicia Richardson, Mark Anderson, and Lynn Long put up with my attempts at humor, keep me accountable, and help me transform rough drafts into polished pieces. Thank you also to Kathy Haueisen, who knows everyone (including my editor) and generously shares her knowledge and important contacts with me. And, as a humor writer, I have to thank the Erma Bombeck Writers' Workshop for making me believe I wasn't just full of wit, a mom with a Mac—I was a writer!

A picture speaks a thousand words, and I owe a heartfelt thanks to my talented childhood friend, Joni Zavitsanos, who lived through many of the stories with me, and put a humorous, artistic spin on each one. Thank you for sharing my vision and for your friendship throughout the years.

Thank you to Kati Hewitt Photography for utilizing every trick in her camera bag to make me look happy and relaxed in my author headshot and feel like a model—at least for a few minutes.

Most importantly, thank you to Trish Lewis, my amazing editor and publisher, and the wonderful group at Van Velzer Press for giving my little book about growing up Greek a chance. You made my dream come true.

Finally, thank you to my readers, the real people who struggle with marriage and motherhood, dog hair and divorce—the strong, resilient household heroes who laugh without fear of the future. My stories are for you.

About the Author

Kalas loves outdoor patios, frozen margaritas, and making people laugh. In her spare time, she drives off into the sunset with her mini Goldendoodle, Romeo, to visit her three grown children (wherever they are) and her parents (who continue to make everyone eat). Through the bittersweet journey of life, she still believes in happily ever laughter—and hopes you do, too.

Visit her at: Tassietypes.com

Love Books?

SUPPORT AUTHORS - buy directly from their publishers. This puts more royalty dollars into the pockets of your favorite author – and gives them time to write their next book.

Visit us for links to our other books as well as many other vibrant publishing companies to find the book for you.

www.vanvelzerpress.com

These ARE The Books You've Been Looking For.

Join our newsletter to get the first scoop on New Book Releases:
Director@vanvelzerpress.com

Made in the USA
Coppell, TX
02 October 2021

63359407R00157